science is
golden

Dr Karl Kruszelnicki

Illustrated by Adam Yazxhi

HarperCollinsPublishers

HarperCollins*Publishers*

First published in Australia in 2008
by HarperCollins*Publishers* Australia Pty Limited
ABN 36 009 913 517
www.harpercollins.com.au

HarperCollins*Publishers*
25 Ryde Road, Pymble, Sydney, NSW 2073, Australia
31 View Road, Glenfield, Auckland 10, New Zealand
1–A, Hamilton House, Connaught Place, New Delhi – 110 001, India
77–85 Fulham Palace Road, London W6 8JB, United Kingdom
2 Bloor Street East, 20th floor, Toronto, Ontario M4W 1A8, Canada
10 East 53rd Street, New York, NY 10022, USA

National Library of Australia Cataloguing-in-Publication data:
Kruszelnicki, Karl, 1948– .
    Science is golden / Karl Kruszelnicki.
    ISBN: 978 0 7322 8536 4 (pbk.)
    Bibliography.
    1. Science – Popular works.
500

Cover photography: Jo Duck
Cover design and internal illustrations: Adam Yazxhi / MAXCO creative
Additional illustrations on p. 248: 'Alien' by Max Yazxhi (aged 5½); 'Space, the final frontier'
    by Zac Yazxhi (aged 2½)
Internal design and layout by Agave Creative Group
Printed and bound in Australia by Griffin Press
70gsm Classic White used by HarperCollins*Publishers* is a natural, recyclable product made
from wood grown in sustainable forests. The manufacturing processes conform to the
environmental regulations in the country of origin, Finland.

6 5 4 3 2 1   08 09 10 11

Contents

Plane Truths

Flying is really safe, but most people wrongly believe that if your plane crashes, your number is up.

Introduction

The world loves to fly and, indeed, needs to fly — over two billion passengers take to the wing in aircraft each year. On average, one in every three people in the world fly each year.

Most people vaguely realise that flying in a jet operated by a major airline is incredibly safe. Flying is about twice as safe as rail travel and six times safer than car travel, when you compare the number of death rates per kilometre travelled. (The figures differ depending on whether all forms of transport are counted worldwide, or just the ones in wealthy countries, and in which year you do the numbers — but this is the general trend for the wealthy countries.) But even though flying is safer than driving, most people wrongly believe that if you are on a plane that crashes, then you are certain to die.

It seems a fairly reasonable assumption (even though it's wrong). After all, a modern plane is a tube made of aluminium only a few fragile millimetres thick — and aluminium can burn quite intensely. The plane also carries up to a few hundred tonnes of fuel that burns very fiercely. It's filled with substances (e.g. cushions and fabrics) that give off very toxic fumes when they burn. And, of course, the plane is moving at close to 1,000 kph. But amazingly, if you look at the statistics, your chances of surviving an aeroplane accident are actually quite good.

Assumption

The word 'assume' means 'to believe something — but without any proof'. It comes from the Latin word *assumere*, which in turn is derived from two roots — *ad* meaning 'towards', and *sumere* meaning 'to take'.

Many of us have forgotten the lesson we learnt in school — that 'assume' makes an 'ass' of 'u' and 'me'. In other words, if you assume something and not check it fully, you could make a mistake.

And this is the long-winded background to people's 'assumption' that aircraft crashes are not survivable. (Sorry about that.)

The Big Stats

For example, in the USA between 1983 and 2000 there were 568 aeroplane crashes. Overall there were 53,487 people on board, with about 95% of them (51,207) surviving. In fact, with about 90% of aeroplane crashes are survivable.

Consider the DC-10, a large twin-aisle, three-engine passenger jet. Over the years, 27 have been destroyed. In 23 of those incidents, 90% of the passengers survived. In 1989, a DC-10 performed an emergency landing at Sioux City, Iowa, after hydraulic failure had

Come fly with me

Over two billion passengers take to the wing
in aircraft each year.
Most people vaguely realise that flying in a jet operated by
a major airline is incredibly safe.

Percentage of accidents / fatalities

	Taxi, load, parked	Takeoff	Initial climb	Climb (flaps up)	Cruise	Descent	Initial approach	Final approach	Landing
		17%						51%	
Accidents	5%	12%	5%	8%	6%	3%	7%	6%	45%
Fatalities	0%	8%	14%	25%	12%	8%	13%	16%	2%
		22%						18%	

Flying is about twice as safe as rail travel and six times
safer than car travel, when you compare the number of
death rates per kilometre travelled.
But even though flying is safer than driving, most people
wrongly believe that if you are on a plane that crashes,
then you are certain to die.

left all control surfaces (e.g. flaps, ailerons and vertical tail stabiliser) immovable. On landing, the plane broke into several sections, a fireball erupted and the passenger section skidded down the runway upside down. You could assume that everybody would die. But 185 of the 296 people on board survived the crash.

In 2006, according to the US National Transport Safety Board, major US airlines carried 750 million passengers over a total distance of 12.8 million km. There were 31 accidents, two with fatalities, leading to a total of 50 deaths. This works out to 3.9 deaths per million kilometres — a very good figure, considering that there were 30,000 takeoffs and landings every day. By the way, only 6% of aviation accidents happen while the plane is cruising at altitude. The remainder happen during takeoff and climbing, or descent and landing.

Modern planes are quite good at surviving blasts. In 1986, a bomb exploded in the luggage compartment of a TWA jet flying over Greece. It landed safely, with only four deaths and 117 survivors. In 1988, on Aloha Flight 243 over Hawaii, a Boeing 737 had a 6 m x 4 m section of its fuselage torn off due to corrosion and fatigue from too many takeoffs and landings. There was only one death.

Statistics and Lies

There are always many different ways to interpret complex real-life situations.

In the case of deaths to passengers on aeroplanes, you could measure the deaths per kilometre flown. This is reasonable, because you have to travel those kilometres to get from A to B. But you can equally make an argument for measuring the deaths per journey or the deaths per hour of travel. In each case, you would get different results.

Why Planes Don't Crash

One major factor that makes road transport so dangerous is the 'nut' behind the wheel. There's not a lot you can do when another vehicle veers from the other side of the road to run into you. You are at the mercy of other drivers, most of whom are poorly trained, and who are quite happy to be distracted by music, phone calls and the like. And some of them drive while under the influence of alcohol or drugs. On the other hand, airline pilots are highly trained and competent individuals, who are somewhat obsessive about following correct safety protocols.

One reason why air travel on a well-maintained plane in a wealthy country is so safe is the 'system'. The air crash investigators, the people running the airline and the government regulators are all keen to investigate all crashes thoroughly. They then learn from these crashes and make the necessary changes to avoid a similar incident from happening again.

For example, in 1987, a fire broke out in the rear lavatory on Air Canada Flight 797. The plane landed, but not before a flash fire erupted throughout the passenger cabin. Twenty-three of the 46 people on board died. As a result, smoke detectors and automatic fire extinguishers are now fitted in all aeroplane lavatories.

First Aviation Accident

The first recorded aviation fatalities occurred on 15 June 1785. Two French balloonists, Jean-François Pilâtre de Rozier and Pierre Romain, died when their balloon crashed while attempting a flight across the English Channel.

Why Planes Do Crash

Planes crash for two main reasons — human error, or component error.

Human error can include mistakes by the engineers doing the maintenance, by the pilots doing the actual flying and by the air-traffic controllers directing the plane.

Component error involves the hardware from which the plane is made. The materials used may have voids or foreign inclusions in the microstructure. The materials could also have been designed badly, with small holes or notches that increase the local stresses. Alternatively, the materials and their design might be perfectly fine, but they may have been assembled wrongly or with poor quality paints, lubricants or glues, allowing them to corrode and weaken.

In general, corrosion accounts for about 30% of failures, material fatigue for 25%, brittle fracture for 15% and overload for about 10%. Other less common component causes include high temperature corrosion, creep (the slow plastic deformation of metal), wear, abrasion or erosion.

Sometimes the causes are very subtle. In one case, a bolt — made from high-strength steel plated with cadmium — fractured. It turned out that hydrogen is released during the plating process. The bolt had fractured because some of the hydrogen got trapped locally in the steel, making it unexpectedly brittle. Once the cause of the failure had been discovered, the treatment was relatively simple. Each and every one of all future high-strength, cadmium-plated steel fasteners of this type, now have to be baked for 24 hours at 175–205°C. This allows the hydrogen to diffuse evenly through the steel, rather than being concentrated near the surface.

Biggest Aviation Disaster

On 27 March 1977, a KLM Boeing 747, while taking off from a fog-bound runway, ran into a taxiing Pan Am Boeing 747 at Los Rodeos Airport on the island of Tenerife, in the Canary Islands. Overall, 583 people died.

Superstitions

Different countries have different superstitions — especially with what are regarded as 'unlucky' numbers.

So Continental Airlines flights don't have a Row 13 — and Air France, AirTran, Iberia and KLM also avoid using the number 13. This number is thought to be unlucky for various reasons. One of the more popular explanations concerns Judas Iscariot, who betrayed Christ at the Last Supper. Judas was supposedly the 13th person to sit at the table.

In the Japanese language, the number '4' sounds like the word for 'death', while the number '9' sounds like the word for 'torture'. So All Nippon Airways flights do not have rows 4 or 9 — but for some unknown reason, they also omit Row 13 (a Christian-based superstition) for good luck. Japan Airlines flights, on the other hand, do not have Row 13, but they do have Rows 4 and 9. Other Asian airlines that omit Row 13 include Malaysian Airlines, Singapore Airlines, Thai Airways and Cathay Pacific. And Korea's Inchon Airport bows to cross-cultural superstitions by not having Gates 4, 13 or 44.

As you can see, there's no real logic or consistency to it all.

An especially obscure superstition is the one against the number 17. In Latin, vixi means 'I lived' — which could be interpreted to mean 'I am dead'. If you rearrange the letters VIXI you get XVII — the number 17 in Roman numerals. So the German carrier Lufthansa misses both Rows 13 and 17. But strangely, the Italian carrier Alitalia keeps Row 17, but leaves out Row 13 — except on their Boeing 777s.

Dealing with good luck is just as irrational. The Chinese consider the number 8 to be lucky, because it sounds like the word 'to become wealthy' (that is why the Opening Ceremony of the Beijing Olympics began at 8 pm on 8.8.08 — 8 August 2008). So when Continental Airlines launched Flight 88 from Beijing to Newark, the air fare for the return trip was US$888. Western culture regards the numbers 7 and 11 as lucky, so Northwest runs Flight 777 from Minneapolis to Las Vegas, while US Airways runs Flight 711 from Pittsburgh to Las Vegas.

Safest Seat?

Where is the safest place to sit in a plane, in the unlikely event of a crash? It all depends on the type of crash — whether it's head-on into a mountain or tail-down into a runway.

In 2007, *Popular Mechanics* magazine looked at the 20 accidents since 1971 that had both survivors and fatalities. They found that, on average, passengers were 40% safer at the back of the plane. When you look closely at their analysis, you find that the 'safety' trend is very variable. In 11 of the 20 crashes, rear-seat passengers did better. But in five of the 20 accidents, people sitting at the very front (in first class or business class) had a better chance of survival. In three cases, there was no real advantage in seating position and, in the last case, the seat positions could not be determined. (If a statistical finding, e.g. rear seats are safer, is very variable, then the finding might not be valid.)

But their statistical analysis ignored one very important factor. There are far fewer passengers in first class than there are in economy. So you would expect fewer numbers of first-class passengers to survive, simply because there are so few of them. For example, a Boeing 747 flying between Sydney and London might have 14 people in first class, 66 in business and 265 in economy.

However, there is one consistent safety issue with regard to seating. If possible, sit within seven seats of an emergency exit. This increases your chances of getting out of the plane quickly, once on the ground. (But of course, the safest seat of all is back at home.) And the safest seat on a plane is probably on a military passenger jet, where the seats face backwards.

Staying Alive — Parts 1 to 4: Clothes, Briefing, Seatbelt and Drugs

There's a lot you can do to help you become a survivor of a plane crash. Remember, most of the deaths do not happen with the initial impact. They happen afterwards — in the fire or during the evacuation.

The first factor is the clothes you wear. Avoid synthetics that can burn and melt into your skin. Instead, make sure that you wear long pants and a long-sleeved top made from natural fibres and sensible leather shoes that cover your entire foot.

Then, pay close attention to the Flight Safety Briefing by the cabin crew — and yes, do count the number of seats to the nearest exit. In my 50-or-so flights per year, I watch the briefing for a few reasons — professional solidarity with a fellow performer, politeness, but most importantly, safety. In an emergency, the cabin may well be pitch-black and full of smoke, and you will be glad that you made the effort. And read the Safety Information Card — to reinforce the message.

It sounds really stupid to be told how to undo a seatbelt. After all, haven't you been using a seatbelt in a car for years? But in an emergency, precision is often lost in a panic. Professor Ed Galea from the University of Greenwich, a leading aviation safety expert, has studied over 2,000 reports from survivors. He found many cases of people in aircraft accidents being simply unable to lift the latch to undo the seatbelt. The seatbelt mechanism in aeroplanes is very different from the seatbelt mechanism in modern cars — it has fewer moving parts and only a simple latch to lift. However, because today's elegant car seatbelt is released with the press of a button, it has more moving parts. Having fewer moving parts in the aircraft seatbelt latch means that it's less likely to fail, which is why aircraft designers chose the simple lift-up latch. In crashes, many passengers have fruitlessly searched for a button to press — but they stayed stuck in their seats because there was no button.

Always leave your seatbelt latched, even if it's a bit loose. In the unlikely event that your plane hits an 'air pocket', you won't get plastered onto the roof.

Don't drink too much alcohol, and under no circumstances take sleeping tablets. In an emergency, you need to have your wits about you. Another advantage in keeping sober is that you will get over the dreaded jet lag sooner.

Staying Alive — Parts 5 and 6: Brace and Plan

In a crash landing, assume the Brace Position in which you fold yourself forward. This reduces the chances of your limbs swinging around, hitting something hard and breaking your bones. It also keeps your upper torso as low as possible, decreasing the possibility of being hit by flying debris. The Brace Position also keeps you from smashing into the seat in front of you, because you are already resting against it. (On the other hand, in some budget airlines the seats are very close together, especially in economy class. This makes it virtually impossible for a tall person to physically get into the Brace Position).

And while it's no big deal to jackknife your body slowly into the Brace Position, it can cause you damage to do it very quickly — as might happen in a crash. By the way, for extra safety, some airlines already have an airbag built into each seatbelt, to stop this 'jackknife effect'. Check out which airlines have this feature and try to fly with them.

Plan what you will do if an emergency is declared, even before the plane takes off. In the event of an evacuation, know where to go and obey all instructions given by the cabin crew. Each member in your travelling party should know what to do. Never, ever, go back to try to find a missing family member. All you will do is slow down the evacuation and endanger other lives. Simply get out of the plane any way you possibly can, go your separate ways and meet up afterwards.

Staying Alive — Parts 7 and 8: Smoke and Oxygen

I am perhaps a little more obsessive than the average passenger, and always carry a fold-up plastic smoke hood in my shirt pocket during a flight. I've never had to use it, but if needed, it seals around my neck filtering the air that I breathe, to keep out all the poisonous chemicals produced in the event of a fire. If you don't have one of these, try to keep below the smoke.

The smoke is surprisingly nasty, thanks to the toxins in the burning plane. In movies and daytime soaps, the heroine stands in the thin smoke in her wispy dress coughing gently, until the square-jawed hero rescues her. In real life, the smoke is so thick that you cannot see. And it's so hot that one single breath can burn your lungs — an effective death sentence. The lack of visibility is the reason why you should count the number of seats to the exit, when the flight attendants ask you to do so during the Safety Demonstration. And remember, even if the smoke is not very thick, it can still steal your strength and render you unconscious.

You should also obey the flight attendants when they ask you to put on your oxygen mask before assisting others. If the cabin loses pressure at cruise altitude, it will take barely 15 seconds before you become unconscious. If you try to help your child or another passenger first, and you take more than 15 seconds, then both of you will be unconscious.

Staying Alive — Parts 9 and 10: Out and More Out

Try to exit the plane in an orderly fashion. Professor Helen Muir of Cranfield University in the UK is a world leader in the field of analysing the factors that influence survival in accidents. She and her team have carried out hundreds of simulated plane evacuations. In one study, the 'passengers' formed orderly lines and exited the plane quickly. She then offered £5 to the first half of the 'passengers' out of the plane. There was a mad rush and lots of congestion at the exits, taking everyone longer to get out of the plane.

Once you are outside, move right away from the plane. Move a few hundred metres away, and upwind if you can, in case the wreckage erupts into a fireball.

Rain Man Was Wrong

In the 1988 movie *Rain Man*, the intelligent and autistic Raymond (Dustin Hoffman) says that Qantas has never had any fatalities, and so he refuses to fly on any airline but Qantas. But he was wrong.

True, Qantas has never had any fatalities with its fleet of passenger jets. But at the time the movie was released, the airline had had eight separate crashes — two in 1951, the other six going back to 1934 — in propeller planes. A total of 55 people died.

Happy Stories

Above all, obey the instructions of the highly trained cabin crew — their main job is not to feed you sweets and drinks, but to keep you alive if something goes very wrong.

In 2005, an Airbus overran the runway while landing in Toronto. Four of the eight exits were unusable. Nevertheless, the flight attendants managed to empty the plane of its 309 passengers and crew in less than two minutes. The plane then erupted into flames, but nobody died.

Think of the Boeing 777 that crash-landed at Heathrow Airport in mid-January 2008. The impact was so savage that it ripped off the right landing gear and rammed the left landing gear up into the very solid root of the left wing (where the wing joins the plane). All 152 passengers and crew survived.

So chocks away — and have a nice flight.

United Airlines Flight 232

Modern aeroplanes usually have several systems to do the same job, so that if one fails, another can take over. For example, the DC-10 has three engines — one on each wing and one on the tail. It also has three hydraulic systems to operate the control surfaces. But all three sets of hydraulic pipes go through the same 20 cm hole near the tail of the plane.

On United Airlines Flight 232 on 19 July 1989, the engine mounted in the tail exploded, throwing debris into the tail of the DC-10 — some of the high-speed shrapnel cutting through all of the three hydraulic pipes.

By an amazing coincidence, Dennis E. Fitch, a DC-10 flight instructor, was travelling as a passenger on this flight. Before the plane had actually begun flying commercially, Dennis had some sessions in the DC-10 flight simulator learning how to fly the new plane. After one session, just for fun, he asked if he could try to fly the 'plane' using only the engines — not the control surfaces. After a long and exhausting session, he worked out that he could turn the plane by running one wing engine at a different speed from the other wing engine. He also worked out that he could lose altitude by slowing all the engines and gain altitude by accelerating them.

He was probably the only person in the whole world who had ever practised flying the DC-10 without control surfaces. Once Flight 232 malfunctioned and began flying erratically, he volunteered his services to the flight crew, who immediately and gratefully accepted. He used his skills to regain a little control over the crippled beast.

After some very scary incidents in the air, he touched down on the shorter runway (barely managing to do so) at Sioux Gateway Airport (the nearest available). The plane was sinking six times faster than normal — 563 m (1,850 ft) per minute as compared to the normal 91 m (300 ft) per minute. It was also coming in at almost twice the normal speed — 240 knots (444 kph) instead of 140 knots (260 kph).

Not only was it a hard landing, the DC-10 didn't land squarely. In fact, it bounced a few times. The tip of the right wing hit first and broke open, spilling fuel which immediately caught fire. The tail section hit the runway very hard and simply broke off. The landing gear and the wing engines were torn off. The passenger-filled fuselage broke into several sections. On the final bounce, the flaming right wing was torn off and the largest section of the fuselage slid sideways along the runway and slowly rolled upside down.

Of the people on board, 185 (including Dennis E. Fitch) survived. However, 111 died, most of them from the repeated impacts of the plane hitting the runway, and some from inhaling toxic smoke.

People survived that day as a result of a number of fortunate coincidences. Dennis E. Fitch — who had trained to fly a DC-10 without control surfaces — was on the plane. The Iowa National Guard were on duty at the airport that day — this meant that 285 people skilled in dealing with emergencies were right on hand. And the accident happened during a change of shift at both the local Trauma Center and the regional Burns Center — effectively, twice as many medical staff were on hand to treat the victims.

It was one of the luckiest plane crashes ever.

References

'Annual statistics show continued improvement in aviation safety', *National Transportation Safety News*, 13 March 2007.

Bibel, George, 'Listen up and fly right', *The New York Times*, 26 January 2008.

Findlay, S.J. and Harrison, N.D., 'Why materials fail', *Materials Today*, November 2002, Vol 5, Issue 11, pp 18–25.

Grossman, David, 'Check your travel superstitions, or carry them on', *USA Today*, 31 October 2005.

Noland, David, 'Safest seat on a plane: PM investigates how to survive a crash', *Popular Mechanics*, 18 July 2007.

Noland, David, '10 plane crashes that changed aviation', *Popular Mechanics*, September 2007.

Wilber, Del Quentin, 'Avoiding plane crashes by crunching numbers: Data mining helps identify subtle flaws', *Washington Post*, 13 January 2008.

Mayan Apocalypse, 2012

The taxi driver was taking me from Melbourne airport into the city. As we chatted, it emerged that he was deeply worried. He had a wife and child, and a new baby on the way — but what was the use of living, he cried. After all, he had read on the internet that Mayan prophecies claimed the world would end in 2012, when his newborn baby would be just five years of age.

Eve of Destruction

Prophecies about the end of the world (or, at the very least, civilisation as we know it) have probably been around forever.

There was a flurry of Destruction Prophecies around the time of the new millennium in the year 2000. For some unknown reason, people seem to think that God wants the Universe to self-destruct whenever there is a bunch of zeros in the calendar date. There was another bunch of Doom and Destruction prophecies for 5 May 2005, when all the planets were supposed to line up — by the way, they didn't line up and, yep, we're still here. And more recently, some people were convinced that the world would come to an end in early 2008 when the planet's population reached 6.66 billion.

In addition to internet sites forecasting the End of Days, there are quite a few books devoted to the topic. These include *Mayan Prophecies* by Adrian Gilbert and Maurice Cotterell (1995) and *2012: Mayan Year of Destiny* by Adrian Gilbert (2006). Two books by José Argüelles, *The Mayan Factor* in 1987 and *The Thirteen Moon Calendar* in 1992, are very imaginative. In 1998, José Argüelles declared that 'Argüelles is dead', and that he was now reborn as 'Valum Votan', some kind of successor to a Mayan ruler. He found a solution to the universal apocalypse that was coming — simply get rid of our Gregorian calendar, adopt some kind of lunar calendar, and all would be well.

Mayan Writings

The invading Spaniards did not have much respect for the Mayans. In 1565, Diego de Landa, a missionary Brother who later became the Bishop of Merida, wrote: 'We found a large number of books in these characters and, as they contained nothing in which were not to be seen as superstition and lies of the devil, we burned them all, which they [the Maya] regretted to an amazing degree, and which caused them much affliction.'

Mayan Society

The Mayan civilisation covered the skinny bit of the Americas between North and South America, ranging from the southern states of Mexico down to western Honduras. Its Classic Period occurred from 250 to 900 AD, so their best years were behind them by the time of the Spanish Conquistador invasion in the 1500s.

Mayan Apocalypse

There has always been someone, somewhere, predicting that the end of the world is near. Prophecies about the end of the world have been around for thousands of years.

The Mayan civilisation covered the skinny bit of the Americas between North and South America, ranging from the southern states of Mexico down to western Honduras.

Extent of the Maya Empire

Gulf of Mexico

Cancun

YUCATAN PENINSULA

Bay of Campeche

CAMPECHE

Caribbean Sea

MEXICO

GUATEMALA

HONDURAS

Pacific Ocean

EL SALVADOR

NICARAGUA

At their peak, the Mayans had the only mature written language ever found in the Americas, spectacular and densely populated cities, and very sophisticated systems of mathematics, astronomy and calendars.

They were marvellous astronomers, observing the skies only with the naked eye. (And disregard what you read in the New Age media — the Mayans did not 'learn astronomy via Atlantis from extraterrestrials'.) Their measurements of the year, the lunar month and the movements of Venus were more accurate than those of the ancient Greeks. On the other hand, they were not quite as accurate as the Greeks in measuring the movements of Mars. And they did not devise either the wheel or the stone arch.

Nonetheless, their calendars were very ingenious.

Calendars 101

According to the dictionary, a calendar is 'a system for organising days into a purpose that is religious, socially, commercially or administratively useful'.

Calendars usually consist of several levels. The first level is usually fairly short — for example, a 'week' made up of seven days. The next level, in our Western Gregorian calendar, is the 'month' made up of several weeks.

It all starts to get really messy when the makers of the calendar try to synchronise it with some regularly occurring natural phenomenon. The Islamic calendar is a lunar calendar, i.e. each month begins with a new moon. The ancient Persians had a solar calendar based on the time it takes for the Earth to make one revolution around the Sun. Our Western Gregorian calendar is basically a solar calendar, with a few fudges (leap years) thrown in to try to keep it in line with reality. Some ancient Egyptian calendars followed the movements of Venus. The 'solar–lunar' calendar (e.g. the Jewish calendar and the Celtic Coligny calendar) that tries to follow the movements of both the Sun and the Moon had to insert an extra month every 19 years to keep it accurate.

Mayan Calendars 101

The Mayans had many calendars, because they saw 'time' as a meshing of sacred or spiritual cycles. They used their various calendars to mark the time between rituals, to try to interpret omens and to predict future astronomical events.

Blame Augustus Caesar for Crazy February

The old Roman calendar was a kind of lunar calendar. The Moon takes about 29.5 days to complete its orbit around the Earth. Therefore, the old Roman calendar had months that were alternately 29 and 30 days long, making it a 'year' of only 354 days. So Julius Caesar's astronomers changed this to months composed alternately of 30 and 31 days. To try to keep in time with the seasons, February had 30 days only in leap years.

Julius Caesar modestly named the month of July after himself. Not to be outdone, Augustus Caesar named August after himself. And to make August as long as July, he stole a day from February and shoved it into August.

The Haab Calendar

At their peak, the Mayans had the only mature written language ever found in the Americas ... and their calendars were also very nice.

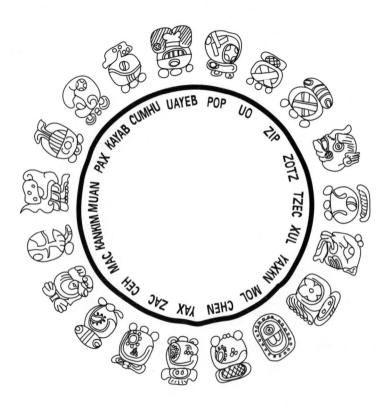

The glyphs of the Mayan months, which start at Pop, plus the five 'unlucky' days at the end of the year called Wayeb.

Mayan Calendars — Part 1: Tzolkin

The most important of the Mayan calendars was the Tzolkin calendar, which is still used in the Guatemalan highlands. It ran for 260 days, with 20 time periods (*winal*) of 13 days.

There are several theories about how this calendar came into existence. The first theory suggests that the Mayans used the numbers 13 and 20 for the days and 'months' because these numbers were important in Mayan society. The second theory claims that the 260-day calendar is significant because it is the length of time that it takes to grow a baby. The third theory claims that 260 days is the period of time between planting the crops and reaping the harvest (but surely this would depend on which crop you planted, and the weather). Another suggestion is that the 260 days of the Tzolkin calendar relate to the length of time that Venus is visible as a morning star.

This calendar began with the Olmec (an ancient pre-Columbian society) before 1200 BC. (We don't know why, but the Olmec society declined rapidly between 400 and 350 BC.) (By the way, the Olmec almost certainly invented the use of rubber balls in sport.)

Each day was unique, with its own patron spirit. So one day might be good for travel but bad for selling.

Mayan Calendars — Part 2: Haab

Another Mayan calendar was the Haab. Because it got fairly close to the actual time that it takes for the Earth to go around the Sun, it's sometimes called a 'vague' solar year. It consisted of 360 days — 18 months, each of 20 days — plus a group of five 'nameless days', called the Wayeb, added at the end of the year. These 'nameless days' were fairly dangerous, and people had to be especially careful about carrying out the proper New Year rituals. For example, during this period, the Mayans were advised against leaving their houses or taking care of their hair.

However, Mayan astronomers completely ignored the extra quarter of a day that it takes the Earth to get back to its starting point. For this reason, the Haab would gradually drift across the seasons.

The Haab calendar matched up exactly with their Tzolkin calendar every 52 Haab cycles or 73 Tzolkin cycles. If you multiply a Haab cycle of 365 days by 52, you get 18,980 days. And if you multiple a Tzolkin cycle of 260 days by 73, you get exactly the same number of 18,980 days. The Calendar Round combined the Tzolkin and the Haab to make a longer cycle (of 52 Haab years or 73 Tzolkin years).

They 'named' the days by having the day number followed by the month — a system used by the ancient Egyptians.

Mayan Calendars — Part 3: Long Count

Which brings us to the calendar that supposedly 'predicts' the end of the world in 2012. According to what you can find on the internet, at 'sunrise on 21 December 2012, the Sun rises to conjunct the intersection of the Milky Way and the plane of the ecliptic'.

One of the several Mayan calendars was called the Long Count. It was set up around 355 BC, and had, as its chosen starting date, the Beginning of the World, 0.0.0.0.0, which corresponds to 11 August 3114 BC — a few thousand years earlier. (However, there are also arguments for 12 and 13 August as the starting date.)

And on 21 December 2012, the Mayan Long Count calendar will read 13.0.0.0.0.

Now here's how it works. Our numbering system is based on 10. But the Mayans had a counting system based on 20. Therefore, most of the 'slots' in their calendar had 20 potential numbers — 0 to 19. The calendar read a little like the odometer in your car's speedometer (which runs from 0 to 9). The extreme right slot (of five slots) would count through the days and when it got to 19 days (0.0.0.0.19) it would reset to zero, the next slot across to the left then increasing by one (to 0.0.0.1.0).

So 0.0.0.0.1 was one day, 0.0.0.1.0 was 20 days, 0.0.1.0.0 was about one year, and 0.1.0.0.0 was about 20 years. Once the calendar reached 1.0.0.0.0, it had clocked up about 400 years. And on 21 December 2012, the Mayan Long Count calendar will read 13.0.0.0.0 (this is the famous 'killer' Mayan date that some people worry about).

Various rock carvings (called 'stela') have been found with Long Count dates on them. Stela C (that's how the archaeologists name them), at the Olmec archaeological site of Tres Zapotes, has one of the oldest Long Count dates found so far — 7.16.6.16.18, corresponding to 3 September 32 BC. Stela 2 at Chiapa de Corzo has the date of 7.16.3.2.13, i.e. 10 December 36 BC.

Maths of the Long Count

The Mayan Long Count calendar began with 0.0.0.0.0. It had five slots which filled up from the right, and working across to the left.

The slot at the extreme right counted the days (or *kin*). It started at zero, going up to 19 days. It had 20 possible values (ranging from 0 to 19), because the Mayans had a counting system based on 20, not 10 as we do. So one day was 0.0.0.0.1, while 19 days was 0.0.0.0.19. On the 20th day, with the *kin* slot already filled up, the *kin* slot reset itself to zero, and the count started on the next slot. So 20 days — the length of their 'month' registered on the Long Count as 0.0.0.1.0.

The next slot counted the months (*winal* or *uinal*) — and there were 18 months in their 'year'. There was a reason for the shift from the 20-system to an 18-system — 20 days x 18 months equals 360 days, which is fairly close to a solar year (which is 365-and-a-bit days). The Mayans didn't need the Long Count calendar to be accurate for years, because their other calendars took care of this. When both the right-hand slots were filled to the maximum, the Long Count read 0.0.0.17.19. This was equal to 17 months, consisting of 19 days (340 days) plus one lot of 19 days, giving a total of 359 days — which was one day less than their year of 360 days.

The next slot to the left (*tun*, or roughly a year) again counted up to 20. So 0.0.1.0.0 was one *tun* (a single 360-day year), while 0.0.19.0.0 was 19 *tuns*.

The second-last slot (*katun*) again counted up to 20. So 0.1.0.0.0 was about 20 years, while 0.19.19.17.19 was about 400 years.

The last slot of all (on the extreme left) was called the *baktun*.

There was the possibility of having a few more slots to the left. They were actually given names, but were never really used much.

The Long Count Calendar

Counting System

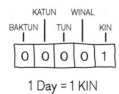

1 Day = 1 KIN

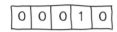

20 Days = 1 WINAL

0	0	1	0	0

360 Days = 1 TUN
(Approx. 1 Year)

0	1	0	0	0

7,200 Days = 1 KATUN
(Approx. 20 Years)

1	0	0	0	0

144,000 Days = 1 BAKTUN
(Approx. 400 Years)

Mayan Numerals

This column shows a
Long Count date of
8.5.16.9.7

(8)

(5)

(16)

(9)

(7)

The Mayan date of
8.5.16.9.7
works out to be
July 14, 156 BC

The Conspiracy Theory ...

The time period between 0.0.0.0.0 and 13.0.0.0.0 is about 5,126 years. Some Mayan archeo-astronomers reckon that the calendar should run up to 13, but others say that it should continue to 20. We don't have enough information to know who is correct — but if it does go up to 20, then this completely destroys the 'End of Days Conspiracy Theory', as far as the year 2012 is concerned. But let's stick to the '13 Conspiracy Theory' for the time being.

The epic claims of the upheavals coming on 21 December 2012 cover a lot of ground. They range from 'nuclear holocaust' to 'Harmonic convergence of cosmic energy flowing through the earth, cleansing it and raising it to a higher level of vibration', and along the way they include 'the death of two-thirds of humanity' and 'the north and south poles will split' — you get the picture. A Doonesbury cartoon reckons that the possibilities are a 'New Age of insight and understanding of mass unification of Divine and Earth-Plane selves' or a 'nuclear annihilation' — but either way, someone will run a 'crafts fair'. Other predictions state that 'a door into the heart of time and space will open', or that we will have 'a moment of collective spiritual birth'.

Mark Twain

In the late 19th century, one Big Problem for those studying the Mayans was the starting date of the Long Count. This is called the Correlation Question — how do you correlate the Mayan Long Count with the Gregorian calendar?

One of the people who solved this problem gave Mark Twain his first writing job. He was the newspaper man Joseph Goodman. In 1897 he proposed that the start date for the Mayan Long Count was in 3114 BC. His work was followed up by Juan Hernandez Martinez and later by Sir John Eric Sydney Thompson in 1927. So in some circles, the Correlation is known as the Goodman Martinez Thompson Correlation or GMT. The so-called GMT Correlation places the Mayan Long Count starting date of 0.0.0.0.0 in 3114 BC.

Of course, this GMT confused the heck out of me when I first came across it, until I realised that it had nothing to do with Greenwich Mean Time.

The Big Finish

However, these scenarios are all very unlikely.

First, the Universe didn't begin on 11 August 3114 BC, but about 13.7 billion years earlier.

Second, when a calendar comes to the end of a cycle, it just rolls over into the next cycle. In our Western society, every year 31 December is followed, not by the End of the World, but by 1 January. So 13.0.0.0.0 in the Mayan calendar will be followed by 0.0.0.0.1 — or Good Ole 22 December 2012, with only a few shopping days left to Christmas.

Third, there are a few Mayan stela that show dates beyond 21 December 2012.

And, finally, it is always remarkably difficult to make predictions, especially about the future, and things that haven't happened yet.

References

Finley, Michael, 'The real Maya prophecies: Astronomy in the inscriptions and codices', http://members.shaw.ca/mjfinley/mainmaya.html.

Jenkins, John Major, 'The how and why of the Mayan end date in 2012 AD', *Mountain Astrologer*, Dec 1994–Jan 1995.

Jenkins, John Major, 'The Maya calendar and 2012: Why should we care?', *New Dawn*, Special Issue No 4.

Sweat Like a Pig

In the past, pigs haven't had very good PR. In the Bible, Leviticus writes, 'And the pig, because it parts the hoof and is cloven-footed but does not chew the cud, is unclean to you.' And both the Jewish and Islamic faiths prohibit the consumption of pork. Today, pigs get even more bad press with regard to their personal hygiene, people disparagingly claiming to '… sweat like a pig'.

Pigs 101

Pigs have a stout body, short legs, a small tail and a thick skin, usually with sparse short bristles. They are also hardy, swift and omnivorous. Their life span can reach 25 years in the wild.

We have been domesticating pigs for thousands of years. Smaller pigs (less than 75 kg) are usually turned into pork, while heavier pigs (100 kg and up) are turned into bacon. In each case, about 75% of the weight of the animal is turned into useable meat.

Domesticated female pigs have a gestation period of just three months, three weeks and three days — and with 10 piglets per litter and two litters per year, can breed very rapidly indeed. The most popular breed of pig is the Yorkshire, or Large White, which emerged in the UK in the 18th century. Today there are about a billion pigs on the planet — about half of them in China, some

Gonna make you sweat!

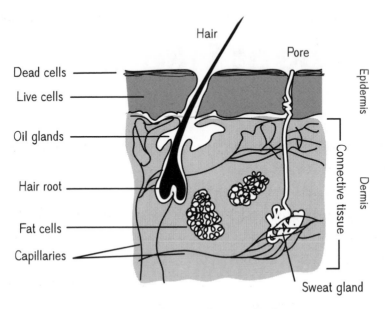

Hair

Pore

Epidermis

Dead cells

Live cells

Oil glands

Hair root

Fat cells

Capillaries

Connective tissue

Dermis

Sweat gland

A cross-section of human flesh

Wild pigs have to wallow in mud because they cannot sweat — contrary to popular belief.

60 million in the USA and 30 million in Brazil. Pigs are not native to North America. They were introduced to the Caribbean islands of the Americas by Christopher Columbus, on his second journey in 1493, and then taken to the mainland in the early 1500s.

Pigs are easy to feed, breed quickly and (for some of us) are delicious to eat.

Sweat 101

We humans (and the other primates, horses and bears) have lots of sweat glands. In fact, horses are the Kings of Sweat.

Sweat is our personal air-conditioning machine. The operating temperature of human beings is 'set' by the hypothalamus in the brain at about 37°C. You can survive if your temperature drops down to about 25°C — a drop of 12°C. But you cannot survive overheating to the same degree. Once you increase your temperature to about 43°C (6°C above normal), you almost certainly won't survive.

Men and women have roughly the same number of sweat glands — about 2–5 million over the whole body, or about 150–350 per square centimetre. When the outside temperature rises, a liquid that is 99% water oozes out of these sweat glands onto the surface of the skin. The remaining 1% of liquid sweat is sodium chloride, other salts, amino acids and a smattering of other chemicals. The sweat then evaporates — cooling your skin.

When you get hot, the temperature sensors in your skin send this 'heat' information to the hypothalamus. It then sends signals down through the spinal cord and into the sympathetic ganglia. In turn, these send signals to the eccrine sweat glands. A few more steps, and cooling sweat starts oozing out of your sweat glands.

All human beings sweat, but there are some differences. Women sweat at a higher temperature than men do, and women also generate less sweat.

Sweat and Emotion

There are two main types of sweat glands. The eccrine sweat glands mainly produce sweat for cooling. However, the apocrine sweat glands produce sweat with added 'special' chemicals. (I remember which gland is which because 'eccrine' starts with the letter 'e', which is also in 'sweat'.)

These special chemicals can have strange effects on other animals of the same species. For example, it has been long known that armpit sweat helps women to synchronise their menstrual cycles. In 2007, it was discovered that just a few whiffs of male human sweat was enough to increase levels of cortisol (a stress hormone) in the blood of women who smelled this male sweat.

Sweat and Exercise

Comparing fit people to unfit people, the fit person will sweat sooner during exertion and at a point when their body temperature is lower.

If you are fit ('fit' in this case means 'acclimatised' to the local temperature as well as having more cardiovascular training), your sweat reflex kicks in sooner (than if you are unfit). Therefore, your core temperature will be at a lower temperature when you start to sweat. This means that you can potentially continue your exertion for a longer period of time before you begin to overheat. So you can run down an antelope, which is a good sprinter but a lousy marathon runner. Indeed, marathon runners can perform better if they are 'pre-cooled' immediately before the race by wearing a special 'cooling' jacket.

However, if you are 'unfit' you will start to sweat at a higher temperature. You will activate your cooling mechanism later — and miss out on the antelope.

People can train to sweat more. The Australian triathlete, Ali Fitch, moved from the cool climate of Sydney to the tropical Northern Territory specifically for 'acclimatisation training'. She increased her rate of sweating from 300 ml/hr to 1,500 ml/hr.

Fatter people sweat more than skinny people. The extra fat acts as an insulator, forcing them to sweat more to lose excess heat.

You can generate several litres of sweat per hour, while working strenuously in a very hot environment. Sweating is good, enabling us to survive in very hot climates.

When It's Too Hot ...

Animals have a few tricks that they can use to cool down.

Panting is the process of breathing more rapidly, and running outside air over the dense network of blood vessels inside the nose. The air becomes saturated with water vapour. This evaporation effect then cools the blood, which enters the general circulation and helps bring the overall temperature down. Panting is more important in smaller animals, such as dogs.

Sweating works well in those animals that have the right sort of sweat glands (water-producing rather than odour-producing). But some animals, such as our friend the pig, simply don't have the right kind of sweat glands. Sweating is more common in larger animals, such as horses.

Wallowing in something wet is quite effective in bringing down the temperature. Pigs and elephants use this method.

Spreading saliva on the fur is used by some rodents and macropod marsupials to cool down.

Thermo-Neutral Zone

Pigs, on the other hand, don't like very high temperatures — because they have very few functional sweat glands and can generate hardly any sweat at all. And they are not very good at dumping heat from their wet mucous membranes in the mouth by panting, which dogs can do quite well. In short, pigs are not very good at handling heat stress. In the wild, pigs tend to feed at night or in the cooler part of the day and rest in the hot part of the day.

Their so-called Thermo-Neutral Zone, where they are very comfortable, runs from 16°C to 22°C. It's also called the 'Zone of Minimal Thermoregulatory Effort'. When an animal is placed in this temperature zone, it can adjust its temperature very easily. To lose or conserve heat, it can open or close blood vessels in its skin. It can spread out all of its limbs or curl up into a ball to adjust its surface area (it is from here that it loses a lot of heat). If the animal has fur, it can lay the individual hairs down flat against the skin or erect them to turn them into a better insulator.

In commercial piggeries, when the temperature rises above this narrow band of 16–22°C, water is dripped, sprayed or misted onto them and fans are activated to cool them down.

Female pigs that are feeding their little newborn piglets in a piggery have extra problems. Because the piglets have a Thermo-Neutral Zone slightly above 35°C, they need to be kept warm with heat lamps. (So even on a hot day, the piglet has to burn energy to keep warm!) The lactating sow needs to eat more to be able to make milk, but the presence of heat lamps means that she eats less. Therefore, she loses more weight than normal during lactation and comes out of lactation with a reduced weight. As a result, she is later to come on heat again, which means that she has both a reduced litter size and an increased chance of spontaneous abortion.

Panting Myth

Dogs do not pant to cool down, by breathing rapidly in and out of their mouth. No, they breathe in through the nose and then out of the mouth. This gives a wonderfully efficient one-way flow of air. They can then increase the surface area exposed to the moving air by dribbling their long tongues out of their mouths.

Pigs Can't Sweat

Pigs like to wallow in seeps, springs, ponds, lakes, creeks and, yes, mud. They do this, not because they enjoy being dirty, but because they like to cool down. Because pigs can get sunburnt the mud also acts as a sunblock. Unfortunately, all this wallowing can cause environmental problems — local soil erosion, degradation of their natural habitats and increased sedimentation in local waterways.

Pigs — Good Press

People who don't like pigs are usually those who don't eat pork.

The Chinese, who eat pork, have the pig as one of the signs of their zodiac. In Greek mythology Demeter is the Goddess of farm animals, including the pig. And Winston Churchill said, 'Dogs look up to us. Cats look down on us. Pigs treat us as equals.'

And to find the highest affection for pigs, look to the owners of Harley Davidson motorbikes. They call their machines 'hogs'.

Despite these problems pigs have to wallow because they cannot sweat — contrary to popular belief.

Which brings us back to the 'sweaty pigs' belief, which is widely held in our culture. In 1979, when Bette Midler was being transformed from a stage performer adored mainly by gay audiences to a mainstream actor, she was playing the role of a self-destructive rock star (modelled on Janis Joplin) in the big-budget movie *The Rose*. She preferred being a movie star, saying, in a *Women's Weekly* interview, 'It's soooo easy. You don't have to get up there for four hours every night and sweat like a pig.'

Widely misunderstood — that's the pig. In fact, even cartoon characters such as Homer Simpson misunderstand them. In 'Lisa the Vegetarian' in *The Simpsons* (Season 7, Episode 5), Homer asks his daughter, Lisa, if she'll ever eat bacon again, and she says 'no'. He then asks if she'll consider eating ham or pork chops, not realising that all these meats come from the same animal, the pig. When Lisa tells him that they do, he does not believe her, and sceptically mocks the pig as a 'wonderful, magical animal'. Doh!

Hot Pigs

Female pigs have a hard time when the weather is too hot. They have a delayed puberty and, overall, a lower reproductive performance. They have a lower conception rate, an increased rate of spontaneous abortion and a reduced litter size.

References

Currie, W. Bruce, *Structure and Function of Domestic Animals*, CRC Press, 1995, pp 321–323.

Hope, Warren, 'Bette Midler goes to Hollywood', *Women's Weekly*, 7 March 1979.

Reece, William O. (Editor), *Dukes' Physiology of Domestic Animals*, Cornell University Press, 12th Revised Edition, 2004, pp 965–969.

Tummaruk, Padet, et al., 'Seasonal effects on the reproductive performance of gilts and sows', *Thai Journal of Veterinary Medicine*, 30 September 2002, pp 19–31.

Wyart, Claire, et al., 'Smelling a single component of male sweat alters levels of cortisol in women', *The Journal of Neuroscience*, 7 February 2007, pp 1261–1265.

Zuger, Abigail, 'More than skin deep', *Sydney Morning Herald* (Health & Science), 14 February 2008, p 22.

Greenhouse Consensus

It doesn't matter whether you call it the Greenhouse Effect, or Global Warming or Climate Change, it's a topic that generates much heat and controversy. And there are many claims and counterclaims.

If your only sources of information were daily newspapers and commercial TV, you would probably think that climatologists (climate scientists) could not agree on anything about the Greenhouse Effect. In other words, you would be led to believe that there was a lot of internal debate amongst these scientists as to whether Global Warming is actually happening.

But this is a nasty little lie. In truth, climatologists almost universally agree that Climate Change is not only real but that we humans are also causing it.

Here Comes the Sun

Practically everything on Earth relies on the Sun. Each second, the Sun burns about 600 million tonnes of hydrogen, turning it into 596 million tonnes of helium. The shortfall of four million tonnes gets turned into energy. Einstein's famous $E = mc^2$ equation tells you how much energy (E) you get if you turn a certain mass (m)

It's getting hot in here

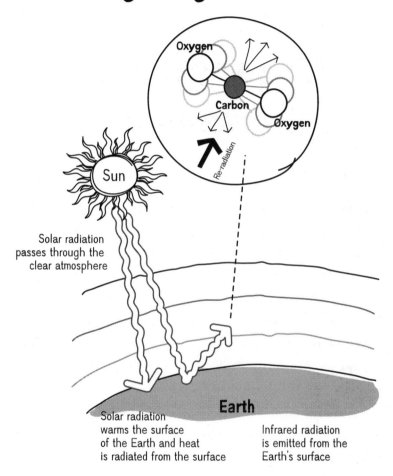

The Greenhouse Effect

Earth has natural greenhouse gases in its atmosphere (such as water vapour, methane and carbon dioxide). These gases are found between the ground and Space. They absorb heat radiated from the surface and in the process re-emit the heat.

into energy. The letter 'c' stands for the speed of light, a very big number — 300,000 km/sec. When you square 'c', you get an absolutely huge number.

The Sun produces about 30 billion billion MW (megawatts) of power. The power density is very intense close to the Sun. Imagine this power appearing on the surface of a virtual sphere that is continually expanding as it travels away from the Sun at 300,000 km/sec. As this radiated power travels, it spreads out and becomes diluted. The Sun is about 149.6 million km from the Earth, so the power that the Sun delivers to the surface of our planet is about one kilowatt in each square metre of radiation.

In Fact, It's a Gas ...

Way back in 1824, the French scientist Joseph Fourier wrote one of the first papers on greenhouse gases. He was followed by John Tyndall in the 1860s, and Svente Arrhenius in 1896.

Today, we have worked out the mechanism of the Greenhouse Effect. It should really be called the Semi-Silvered Mirror Effect (but then it would sound like the title of a romantic ballad).

The Sun heats up the surface of both the Earth and the Moon — each of which is the same distance from the Sun. The surfaces of the Earth and the Moon then radiate their warmth back into Space until, eventually, a balance is reached. So how come the Earth has an average temperature of about +15°C, while the Moon is much colder at −15°C?

The answer is the Natural Greenhouse Effect.

If there were no atmosphere, the average surface temperature on Earth would be −15°C — same as the temperature on the Moon. Because the Moon has no atmosphere, all the energy that its surface radiates out into Space actually manages to reach Space.

However, our planet has natural greenhouse gases in our atmosphere (e.g. water vapour, methane and, yes, carbon dioxide).

These gases, located between the ground and Space, absorb heat radiated from the Earth's surface. They then re-emit the heat.

If the gases sent all of this re-emitted heat straight out into Space, the average surface temperature of the Earth would still be about −15°C. But the greenhouse gases send half into Space and reflect half back down to the ground. (This is because half of the 'field-of-view' of the carbon dioxide molecules is the Earth's surface and the other half is Outer Space. Imagine that you are standing in the middle of an empty desert. If you look in all directions, half of everything you see is the desert floor, the other half is the sky.) The greenhouse gases act like a semi-silvered mirror, which lets some heat through and reflects some heat back. Therefore, the more greenhouse gases that there are in the atmosphere, the more heat is 'reflected' down to the ground.

These natural greenhouse gases lift the average surface temperature of the Earth by about 30°C to a more pleasant +15°C.

Carbon Dioxide

It's normal to have natural greenhouse gases in the atmosphere. The big problem is that we humans have pumped additional amounts of greenhouse gases into the atmosphere.

Around 1750, carbon dioxide levels in the atmosphere were approximately 280 ppm (parts per million). Then modern industrialisation took off. We burnt fossil fuels, pumping up carbon dioxide levels worldwide by 36%, i.e. from about 280 ppm in 1750 to around 380 ppm in 2008. This might not seem much in terms of the total atmosphere, but increases so rapid and so high haven't been seen for nearly a million years. (We have very accurate records of carbon dioxide levels dating back about a millon years. This has been made possible through the analysis of ancient air bubbles trapped in the Antarctic ice.)

Throughout the 20th century two bad things happened because

of the additional amount of carbon dioxide and other greenhouse gases in the atmosphere.

First, the temperature rose by about 0.6°C. Second, the ocean level rose by an average of about 20 cm. About half of this 20 cm rise is caused by the melting of land glaciers. And as the oceans warm, the water expands causing a further 10 cm rise.

But what about all the geologists, meteorologists and other scientists who claim that there is no such thing as Global Warming or that, if there is, carbon dioxide has nothing to do with it? The answer is that they are not climatologists — they are talking outside their area of expertise.

But It's So Small ...

Since 1750, carbon dioxide has increased by 100 ppm. This is a very small fraction, equal to one part in 10,000. Some sceptics ask how such a small increase of just one gas in the whole five trillion tonnes of atmosphere can have any effect at all.

But think about a car weighing one tonne, i.e. 1,000 kg or 1,000,000 g. A big handful of long, sharp nails weighs about 100 g. If you were then to wedge the sharp nails hard up against the four tyres of a car and then drive the car, you would end up with four flat tyres. Something made up of just 100 ppm caused this devastating effect on the car.

And antibiotics and other drugs can have very powerful effects at concentrations much lower than 100 ppm.

So yes, the amount of extra carbon dioxide as a percentage of the total atmosphere is small, but the theoretical mechanisms for how it would affect Global Warming have been calculated, and they agree very closely with what we see happening.

If You Have a Dog, Don't Bark

Now an important thing to realise in this Greenhouse Consensus debate is the role of the specialist.

My Polish parents had a saying, 'If you have a dog, don't bark'. (The English equivalent is 'There is no point having a dog and barking yourself'.)

In other words, a specialist is usually an expert in a particular field. You would not expect a specialist in one field to be an expert in another field. So if you need some carpentry done, you would call a carpenter. You wouldn't expect a builder to also be a plumber, nor would you expect a plumber to also be a chef. These are all different fields of expertise.

The saying also applies to health. When I was working in the hospital system, I learnt the truth of an old medical saying: 'If there's a single treatment for something it usually works. But if there's a bunch of treatments, then none of them really works.' For example, there are many treatments for psoriasis, but none of them are cures. However, there is a single treatment for appendicitis — removal of the appendix. And it usually works.

Now think about it. Who would you ask to remove the diseased appendix? You would definitely consult a medical person, not a plumber, a builder or a chef. But what kind of medical person do you consult? You would not consult a pathologist, an oncologist, a radiologist, a haematologist or an immunologist — even though they are all health professionals. The appropriate person to consult is a surgeon.

So treat the discussion on climate in the same way. If you want an opinion on climatology — ask a climatologist. Meteorologists, virologists, botanists, metallurgists, geologists and physicists are all scientists. But they are not experts in the field of climatology. The only true expert in this field is a climatologist.

The Climatologists Speak

Among climatologists, there is agreement that carbon dioxide levels are increasing. They also agree that this is raising temperatures and ocean levels.

On 3 December 2004, Dr Naomi Oreskes from the University of California analysed 928 scientific papers dealing with 'global Climate Change' that had been published in peer-reviewed journals between 1993 and 2003. Not one of these 928 papers disagreed with the consensus position, even though they may have disagreed on minor details. To quote the paper, 'Remarkably, none of the papers disagreed with the consensus position.'

Since then, climatologists have become more convinced about their stand on 'Climate Change'.

So why do half of the articles about Climate Change in the popular, non-scientific press claim that climatologists are deeply divided over the fundamental concepts of the Greenhouse Effect?

Consensus

The word 'consensus' means 'general agreement'. It comes from the Latin verb *consentire*, meaning 'to agree'.

Why the 'Debate'?

Because, according to The Royal Society, huge companies that make their profits from the burning of fossil fuels stoke the fires of deliberate disinformation. And they start with the blatant lie that climatologists have not reached a consensus.

The Royal Society, which has had Sir Isaac Newton and Albert Einstein as members, is the oldest and most prestigious scientific society in the world. It is also deeply conservative.

On 4 September 2006, Bob Ward, the senior manager for Policy Communication at The Royal Society, wrote to Nick Thomas, the director of corporate affairs for ExxonMobil in the UK. This is the very first time since The Royal Society was founded in 1660 that it has written to a company to challenge its activities.

ExxonMobil is not just any company. In 2007, it was the largest company in the whole world, with a revenue of US$404.5 billion.

Mr Ward asked why ExxonMobil paid millions of dollars to groups that 'misrepresented the science of Climate Change by outright denial of the evidence'. Such a strongly worded letter is very unusual for The Royal Society. In essence, The Royal Society accused ExxonMobil of funding mistruths. In the letter, Bob Ward wrote, 'ExxonMobil last year provided more than $2.9 million to organisations in the United States which misinformed the public about Climate Change through their websites.' He further wrote, '… the statements in your documents are not consistent with the scientific literature.'

On the other side of the Atlantic Ocean, ExxonMobil gave $50,000 to the International Policy Network, a group that claims that the scientific community is deeply divided on the issue of Climate Change. ExxonMobil has also provided lavish funding to many other climate sceptic groups around the world.

Exxon (before it merged with Mobil in 1999) participated in a 1998 meeting at the American Petroleum Institute. A memo from this meeting described the strategy of supporting the climate sceptic groups by providing 'logistical and moral support … thereby raising questions about and undercutting the prevailing scientific wisdom'. Paul Krugman wrote in *The New York Times*: 'The people and institutions Exxon Mobil supports aren't actually engaged in climate research. They're the real-world equivalents of the Academy of Tobacco Studies in the movie *Thank You for Smoking*, whose purpose is to fail to find evidence of harmful effects.'

Mistakes Do Happen ...

But what if it turns out that, even with the best intentions, the climatologists are wrong? After all, everybody can make mistakes — and scientists are no exception.

For example, until the 1960s, geologists believed that the continents were locked in place on the surface of the globe — but they were wrong. Once the hard data was available, they quickly admitted their mistake. Today we know that the continents drift around the surface of the globe at roughly the speed that your fingernails grow — about 5–10 cm per year.

In the same way, even though the overwhelming majority of climatologists agree on the fundamentals of Global Warming, there is a microscopic possibility that they could be wrong. (I use the term 'microscopic possibility' in the sense that there is a microscopic possibility that the Sun will not rise tomorrow, or that a warm lake in a warm climate will spontaneously freeze over.)

But because Climate Change has been studied very closely for a long time, in this case, the scientific consensus is almost certainly correct. This leaves us with the hot problem of what to do about it.

Doubt is Our Product

In 1969, a Tobacco Industry memo stated 'Doubt is our product'.

Professor Robert N. Proctor, from Stanford University, discussed this in the symposium 'The Sociopolitical Manufacturing of Scientific Ignorance' at the annual meeting of the American Association for the Advancement of Science in San Francisco on 18 February 2007.

By the middle of the 1950s, there was medical and

scientific consensus that smoking caused lung cancer. But Big Tobacco (the combined tobacco companies) undermined this consensus very effectively in the public eye for several decades. They funded sceptics, funded bad research that claimed that most lung cancers were actually caused by asbestos or the keeping of birds, and funded 'health' reassurance campaigns that ran advertisements in the medical and general press. For a few decades, Big Tobacco succeeded in their goal.

Professor Proctor said: 'Millions of people in the 60s, 70s and 80s didn't know that tobacco caused lung cancer and heart disease. An increasing number knew, but not everybody knew. And not everyone knew because the industry was manufacturing doubt, fomenting ignorance. Industry executives created a climate of untruth that people bought into and died from.'

I was one of the people who got tricked, even though I had a degree in science, and was supposedly well educated. I took up smoking in the early 1970s. In the mid-1970s, a friend told me that smoking was unhealthy. I didn't believe her, but agreed to look it up in the scientific literature. I did, and very quickly realised that I had been fooled by Big Tobacco and promptly gave up smoking.

Big Tobacco still hasn't stopped spinning their line in the 21st century, more than half a century after the consensus on the dangers of tobacco was established.

In 2003, the *British Medical Journal* (BMJ) published, in good faith, a paper that supposedly discredited the dangers of passive smoking. It apparently showed that the spouses of smokers had the same risks of lung cancer and heart disease as the spouses of nonsmokers. Only later did it become apparent that the data had a 25-year gap, during which the spouses' exposure to second-hand smoke could not be verified. It was then revealed that the author's funding came from Big Tobacco, via the innocuously named Center for Indoor Air Research. And even later it emerged that the author was paid to 'consult' for lawyers who acted for the tobacco companies R.J. Reynolds and Philip Morris. In August 2006, a US Federal Judge referred to this specific BMJ paper as a superb example of how Big Tobacco still used criminal racketeering and fraud to cover up the dangers of tobacco.

Perhaps Big Oil and Big Coal also have the motto of 'Doubt is our product'.

References

Adam, David, 'Royal Society tells Exxon: Stop funding Climate Change denial', *The Guardian Weekly*, 20 September 2006.

Enstrom, James E., et al., 'Environmental Tobacco Smoke and tobacco related mortality in a prospective study of Californians, 1960–98', *British Medical Journal*, 17 May 2003, pp 1057–1061.

Krauss, Clifford, 'Exxon accused of trying to mislead public', *The New York Times*, 4 January 2007.

Krugman, Paul, 'Enemy of the planet', *The New York Times*, 17 April 2006.

Oreskes, Naomi, 'Beyond the Ivory Tower: The scientific consensus on Climate Change', *Science*, December 2004, Vol 306, No 5702, p 1686.

Oreskes, Naomi, 'Undeniable Global Warming', *The Washington Post*, 26 December 2004, p B07.

Timmons, Heather, 'British science group says Exxon misrepresents climate issues', *The New York Times*, 21 September 2006.

Finger Lifting Good

The 'Finger Lift' is a fairly common party game. Basically, four people try to lift another person, each of them lifting with just one finger. At first they can't. After the group performs some kind of ritual they can then magically lift the person. Is it really magic or did they get in touch with the Spiritual Universal Lifting Force? Nope, it's a trick.

Stiff as a Board, Light as a Feather

The Finger Lift also goes under the name of 'Stiff As a Board, Light As a Feather'. It's used harmlessly enough by primary school kids during sleepovers and by high school students trying to impress each other. Unfortunately, it's also used by people trying to push a spiritual barrow in order to lift some money from you.

If you have been part of a Finger Lift or have seen it done by others, your memory of the marvellous event is utterly precise — and utterly wrong.

The subject (henceforth known as the 'liftee') sits in a chair or on a table, or lies down on the floor. Then four people gather around and try to lift the liftee, each using just one single finger. As you would expect, the foursome is less than awesome and can't lift the person.

Then the voodoo begins.

First, you chant a song or rub your own two hands together, or pile all eight hands of the potential lifters one at a time on top of the head of the liftee, or press on their shoulders — or something. It doesn't matter exactly what it is — some kind of silly ritual that doesn't make any sense is always performed.

The next step makes a lot of sense. You are instructed to count in or chant a song and then, at a certain point, to lift. And — lo and behold — your fingers acquire magical strength, enabling you to lift the person effortlessly into the air.

Giving the finger

The 'Finger Lift' is a fairly common party trick that involves four people trying to lift another person, each of them lifting with just one finger. At first they can't, but after a ritual is performed, magically the person is lifted.

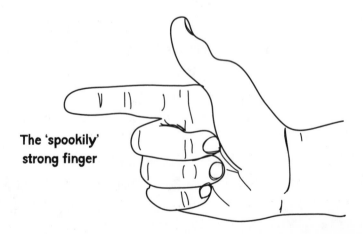

The 'spookily' strong finger

History of finger Lifting

Lynne Kelly gives a lovely debunking of the Finger Lift in her book, *The Skeptic's Guide to the Paranormal*. She mentions that on 31 July 1665, Samuel Pepys recorded how a friend saw some French schoolgirls do this trick. 'This is one of the strangest things I ever heard, but he tells me of his owne knowledge, and I do heartily believe it to be true.' The schoolgirls sang this song while doing the Finger Lift:

Voyci un corps mort,
Royde comme un baston,
Froid comme marbre,
Léger comme un esprit.
Levons te au nom de Jesus Christ.

The famous sceptic, James Randi, translated the song as:

Here is a corpse,
Stiff as a stick,
Cold as marble,
Light as a ghost.
Let us lift you in the name of Jesus Christ.

So the trick has been around for centuries, but how does it work?

There are three answers — timing, the natural underestimated strength of your fingers and poor memory.

1 — Timing

The trick is *always* done in two steps — the first with no coordination, the second with exact timing.

There are lots of videos of the Finger Lift on YouTube, one of them claiming that 'it's an old Romanian trick', while others have Chinese or Africans doing it. Whatever country they come from, the participants all use the sequence of no timing followed by exact timing.

In the first attempt to lift the liftee, there is no effort to get everybody to do the lift at the same instant. In fact, there may be deliberate vague misdirection, along the lines of 'so go ahead, try to lift'. And in all of the videos on YouTube, you can see that the lifters are very much out of sync with each other. This means that for the brief instant that each person is trying to lift the subject by themselves, each of them is fruitlessly trying to lift the entire 50–80 kg weight of the subject on one finger.

However, for the second successful attempt, the timing is very precise. The purpose of the chanting of numbers, a prayer or a song is not to Unleash the Power Within — it's actually meant to synchronise the four potential lifters into one single lifting unit. And there is usually a countdown to the final lift. So all four lift as one, each having to lift only 12–20 kg with their chosen finger.

2 — Finger IS Strong

The second factor is the actual strength of your fingers.

Louis Cyr, the oldtime French Canadian strongman (1863–1912), could lift 553 lb (250.8 kg) with a single finger (his right middle finger). He performed this feat on 8 May 1896. Warren Lincoln Travis, an American vaudeville strongman of the early 1900s, lifted 560 lb (254 kg) with a single finger on his 50th birthday. Using two fingers, he lifted 881.5 lb (399.8 kg).

Each of these strongmen could easily lift the weight of three people with one finger.

Strongman to Cop to Strongman

Louis Cyr, the Canadian strongman, had a father of average size. He got his strongman genes from his mother's side. She was 1.85 m tall and weighed 120 kg, and her father was 1.93 m tall and weighed 118 kg. Louis himself wasn't very tall at 1.78 m, but he weighed 144 kg and, apparently, it was nearly all muscle.

At the age of 17, he lifted a heavily laden tractor out of the mud. He entered the strongman circuit and won his first competition by lifting a granite boulder weighing 217.7 kg. At the age of 20, he broke up a knife fight and carried the two offenders to the police station — one under each arm. He was offered, and accepted, a job with the Montreal police, which he held for two years before going on tour again. He did this successfully for many years, before dying of kidney disease. The great strongman, Joe Weider, wrote a book about him, *The Strongest Man in History: Louis Cyr, 'Amazing Canadian'*.

3 — Poor Memory

The third factor is our very fallible human memory, which then later embroiders the event to make it more impressive.

Every person who has described their experience to me has expressed amazement at the strange mystical powers that gave them the ability to not only lift the subject into the air, but also to hold them there effortlessly.

But every time I have seen it done, in real life and on YouTube, the lifters just barely got the subjects off the ground. And then, they did not hold them up for any length of time and, in fact, almost dropped them in their haste to get them down to the ground again.

So the Finger Lift experience gets the rose-coloured glasses treatment with the passage of time.

The Finger Lift party trick has made it into popular culture with appearances in *South Park* (the 'Marjorine' episode) and in the film, *The Craft*. In each case, it was associated with exotic witchcraft, not prosaic timing.

But the simple explanations really give the finger to the myth.

References

Kelly, Lynne, *The Skeptic's Guide to the Paranormal*, Sydney: Allen & Unwin, 2004, pp 236–238.

'Poosh 'em up', *Time*, 18 August 1941.

All Fire,
No Power

Cars need fuel to run. And fuel has never been free. So for the more than a century that cars with petrol engines have been around, much has been done to improve fuel economy. With lots of hard work, this has been achieved. However, don't believe the easy, drop-a-pill-into-your-fuel-tank claims — they are just a con.

The People Who Know

The alarm bells should ring whenever you hear or read the slogan 'easy improvement in fuel economy'.

The US Federal Trade Commission for the Consumer — a really good source of reliable, trustworthy information — has tested over a dozen different categories of 'gas-savers'. These products all claim to operate by modifying some part of the engine's working cycle.

The US government is frankly sceptical about these products, their laboratory tests over the past 30 years or so showing that these products don't work.

The Car Engine

After doing some tinkering on a car engine, I am always slightly astonished if the engine actually works again. There is something quite amazing about a collection of several hundred lifeless metal and plastic parts that spring into life and keep on spinning by drinking a brownish liquid.

The mechanism of a car engine starts in the fuel tank. The fuel is pumped to the engine and then turned into tiny droplets, to make a mist or vapour with an initial ratio of petrol to air of about 1:15. This vapour is then sent inside the engine and compressed to a volume between eight and 12 times smaller. Then, while it is compressed, it is ignited at exactly the right moment by a spark plug. As the petrol–air vapour burns explosively, it expands in volume, pushing the piston

Have I got a booty-fuel deal for you!

It might restore performance.

It could potentially help your engine.

It may increase your fuel efficiency,

and, it possibly could make you go faster.

BUT …

It DEFINITELY WILL

lighten your wallet!

Super-slick fuel additive

away. The piston is connected to the crankshaft, which rotates. This rotary motion is passed to the gearbox, then down the rest of the drive train until it finally rotates the wheels, and makes the car move.

This is how fuel turns into motion.

There are many points along this chain where you can increase your fuel economy.

We have learnt more about the car petrol engine in the past 20 years than we did in the whole of the previous 80 years. Computers continually tune the engine, hundreds of times each second, to get the best combination of power, economy and emissions. Depending on the intended use of the engine, one of these three is optimised. Therefore, a sports car might sacrifice a little economy to get more power, while a hybrid might aim for maximum economy. And car manufacturers always have to comply with the emissions regulations of the country in which they are selling the car.

Petrol or Gasoline

In the UK and Australia, the liquid that you put into your tank is called 'petrol'.

In the USA, 'petrol' or 'petroleum' is 'rock oil' — the stuff that comes out of the ground. When it is refined into a liquid that goes into your tank, it is then called 'gasoline'. This is usually shortened to 'gas', even though it's not a gas, it's a liquid.

The English language must be so confusing for people trying to learn it as a second language.

1 — The Liquid Fuel

Some 'gas-savers' are fuel additives — stuff you tip into the fuel tank. But there are also devices that you fit on, or in, the fuel line that runs from the tank to the engine. These fuel line devices include heaters or coolers, magnets to 'correctly align the molecules' and even exotic metal alloys from secret Russian laboratories. With this last one, the fuel is supposed to wash over the metal alloy, pick up tiny amounts of the secret metal and carry it into the combustion chamber where it 'improves' your fuel economy.

US Federal Trade Commission engineers have tested virtually every one of these 'gas-savers'. Not one has made any difference.

And think about the fuel line heaters and coolers. Some salespeople reckon that you can improve your fuel economy by heating the fuel, while others reckon that you need to cool the fuel. They can't both be right.

Computers in Cars

Computers in cars have enormously improved the power, economy and emissions of the engine — a good thing.

However, there is a downside. If the computer dies, the owner has to pay several thousand dollars to replace it, as it cannot usually be repaired (under our current economic and technological system). You can buy a lot of fuel for several thousand dollars.

2 — Fuel–Air Mist Mixture

The 'ideal' fuel–air ratio is about 1:15. With too much air, the engine runs too hot and emissions increase. With too much fuel, economy decreases, emissions increase and raw unburnt fuel accumulates on the inside of the cylinder walls. This fuel can wash off the lubricating oil between the cylinder wall and the piston, increasing wear.

One 'gas-saving' device, the Air-Bleed device, allows small quantities of extra air into the fuel–air mixture, supposedly allowing less fuel in and, hopefully, giving better fuel economy. All it really does is overheat the engine and worsen the emissions out of the tailpipe. 'Vapour Bleed' devices do the same thing, but first run the air through a liquid, such as water, or water and antifreeze, or something exotic. Once again, neither of these Bleed devices has ever been proven to work.

Other odd devices in this category of 'gas-savers' are 'Mixture Enhancers' (whatever 'enhancing' the mixture means). They claim to improve fuel economy by increasing the turbulence of the fuel–air mist. (In reality, you want to reduce the turbulence.) They are placed inside the intake pipes before the fuel–air mist reaches the combustion chamber. These 'Mixture Enhancers' can be truly bizarre, with fans, tiny propellers, metal tubes with fins, and even a metal plate with holes in it. You guessed it, they don't work either.

The 'Liquid Injection' device has a little tank of water or methylated spirits hooked into the intake system of the engine. This process does give a very small improvement in fuel economy, but at a cost of increasing engine emissions — and extra dollars.

3 — Internal Engine Modification

These devices usually have a mechanism to reduce the fuel burn by shutting down a few of the cylinders, when you don't need full power.

Big car companies have been trying to perfect this procedure for a few decades. In the early days, they had problems with engines self-destructing. Recently, they have managed to shut down a few cylinders without destroying the engine.

Can you believe that a backyard mechanic, without the massive resources of the car companies, could make such a mechanism? Some of the devices tested provided a tiny increase in fuel economy, but with an increase in emissions and significantly less reliability.

4 — Oils and Oil Additives

Also available are expensive 'special' oils that supposedly reduce friction between the moving parts inside the engine, and so improve fuel economy. Expensive oil additives are also used.

And yes, none of them work.

5 — Ignition Devices

At a specified time in the cycle of the engine's operation, the spark plug has to fire.

There have been many devices on the market, which 'improve' this spark — to make it fire for longer, or at a higher or lower voltage, in fact any claim that will convince you to hand over some money. They don't work either.

6 — Driving Habit Modifiers

These devices monitor how you accelerate through the gears, and/or how hard you press the accelerator while cruising at a fixed speed. They then give you some kind of signal (a light or a sound) to tell you to drive more gently, or to change up or down a gear.

Yes, these devices do give a very modest improvement in fuel economy and do not increase emissions. But they are expensive. In half an hour you can learn how to do this by yourself without the help of a modifier.

Be Sceptical

The US Federal Trade Commission also provides very practical advice. Be wary, they write, of the following types of advertising claims — that the product improves fuel economy by 20% (they do not and cannot), and that various government bodies have endorsed the device. You should also be wary of companies that provide glowing personal testimonies about their products.

Very few customers have the training or access to the appropriate facilities to perform comparative fuel economy tests accurately. In the case of Firepower, an Australian company (which sold a $1.50 pill as a fuel additive), one glowing testimonial came from a company that coincidentally had the same address as Firepower, while another came from 'Joseph and Julie in Fiji'.

In September 2005, the American magazine *Popular Mechanics* published an article about the testing of several 'gas-savers'. None showed any improvement, most reduced the engine's horsepower, and one caught on fire, needing fire extinguishers to put out the blaze. The author, Mike Allen, pointed out that your engine already burns over 99% of the fuel, because less than 1% of the unburnt or partially burnt fuel leaves the engine block.

There are no easy improvements. Indeed, one Australian manu-facturer moved heaven and earth in the manufacture of a recently launched car trying to get the fuel economy to less than 11 litres/100 km — a number psychologically significant to new car buyers. If a $1.50 pill really did provide a 20% improvement, they would have tried it.

Firepower

Firepower, the Australian-based company, built its considerable and temporary fortune by selling a pill that would improve your fuel economy (by up to 42%!). All you had to do was add it to your petrol tank. Firepower seems to be the latest in a long line of companies that appear with a miraculous product, make a lot of money, and then vanish, leaving a lot of people without their money.

Firepower first burst into the media in November 2006, with the announcement of a $3 million sponsorship of the Rabbitohs, a Sydney rugby league club. Indeed, Russell Crowe (a part owner of the Rabbitohs) announced this sponsorship on Jay Leno's *Tonight Show* in the USA.

Firepower also sponsored the Sydney Kings basketball team, which gratefully renamed itself the Firepower Sydney Kings.

Since then, Firepower has been linked to federal and state politicians and bureaucrats, the Australian government agency Austrade, the former Australian Prime Minister John Howard, the former Australian ambassador in Pakistan, the arms trade in Romania, former German heads of Haliburton, the Western Force Rugby Club, the Tongan National Rugby team and even the Australian Superbike Championship, the Australian V8 Supercar racing team and the Porsche Carrera Cup.

At one stage, Firepower was supposedly worth $3.5 billion — pretty amazing for an empire built on a little brown pill (costing $1.50) that you pop into your fuel tank, and which supposedly increases your car's fuel economy. But there were problems — they refused to get their

What a Fool I Was ...

And yes, I myself have been fooled. I bought an expensive liquid injection device for my very first car, a Beetle. And later I tried a few fuel additive products — and I was a sucker for secret Russian metal alloy pipes. I have also tried both Teflon and molybdenum disulphide oil additives. Oh yes, I also tried various spark improvers. Being slightly obsessive, I measured the fuel economy, both with and without the devices for several months — and none of them made any difference.

Why did it take me so long to learn my lesson? I guess that I was being 'fuelish' ...

Real Fuel Economy Improvement

There are many things that you can do to improve fuel economy.

Drive intelligently to anticipate the driving situation on the road ahead. Drive at 90 kph rather than at 110 kph — you will use 10% less fuel. (Unfortunately, it's very unsafe to drive at such a slow speed on a freeway when everyone else is driving to the speed limit.) Higher gears and cruise control can help, as does car maintenance. And keep the pressure of the tyres up. If all four tyres are 25% below normal, you lose 5% fuel economy. Keep the air filter clean. A dirty air filter can drop your fuel economy by 10%. And remove excess weight from the boot. If you 'store' junk in the boot of your car, it's just dead mass. Every time you accelerate, you have to burn extra fuel to bring the speed of this junk from zero to cruising speed.

Try not to drive during peak hour. By avoiding traffic jams, you can save 50% of the fuel.

Try to combine errands, to take one trip instead of three — or walk or ride a bike. And, of course, you can save 100% of the fuel by not taking the car.

References

Allen, Mike, 'Looking for a miracle: We test automotive "fuel savers"', *Popular Mechanics*, September 2005, pp 104–108.

'Gas-saving tips', *The New York Times*, 6 August 2006.

Magnay, Jacquelin and Ryle, Gerard, 'Castles in the air: A life to crow about', *Sydney Morning Herald*, 7 June 2008, p 8.

Ryle, Gerard, 'Firepower link to dead dictator and former spy', *Sydney Morning Herald*, 30 January 2007, p 5.

Ryle, Gerard, 'Petrol pill claims debunked 15 years ago', *Sydney Morning Herald*, 2 February 2007.

US Federal Trade Commission: Protecting America's Consumers, Facts for Consumers, '"Gas-Saving" Products: Fact or Fuelishness?': http://www.ftc.gov/bcp/edu/pubs/consumer/autos/aut10.shtm.

Wag the Dog

It should be pretty easy to read the emotions of a dog. After all, it has been called 'Man's Best Friend'. However, if the tail is stiff and doesn't move, the ears are tucked in close to the head, and the body held in a tight stance, then you should keep away. On the other hand, if the dog's tail is wagging, and the ears are pricked up and the body is wriggling like a can of worms, then it's probably safe to pat the dog.

But what about those occasional cases of a dog still biting, even though its tail is wagging? Well, recent research has given us another clue — the equivalent of fine print in a contract — to help us read the telltale signs of the dog's wagging tail.

Left Not Equal to Right

It all goes back to the nervous system and its lack of perfect symmetry. The left side of the body and the brain are quite similar to the right side, but with some definite differences. Both the nerve pathways that run into the brain, and the brain itself, are wired up in a non-symmetrical way.

The ancient Greeks noted that some soldiers who suffered damage to the left side of their brain were not able to speak

Wag the Dog

In general terms, the left brain is more linked to approaching something, whereas the right brain is more involved in withdrawing, or moving away.
Overall, it appears that the right brain (which controls the left side of the body) is more responsive to stimuli that are negative, and to oddities and emergencies and threats.

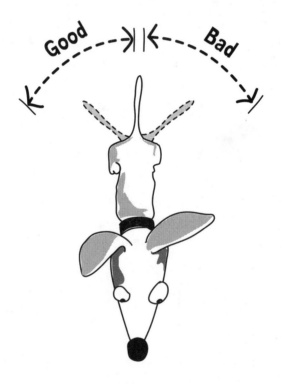

The Golden Rule Is:
Tail to the (dog's) right, it's all right,
Tail to the (dog's) left, it's best you left.

properly. They didn't know it back then, but the 'language' area of nearly all right-handed people is on the left side of the brain.

By 1861 the French physician Paul Broca had found this specific area in autopsies on some of his patients who had lost their speech. (Mark Dax had made the same discovery in 1836, but Broca got all the credit.) However, around the same time in the mid-1800s, it was also common medical knowledge that the brain was cross-wired to the body. So they knew that the left side of the brain controlled the limbs on the right side of the body (and vice versa).

And this leads to behaviour that is specific to one side of the body. For example, most people are right-handed. In the case of human beings, we have been this way for a long time — Bronze Age weapons and tools are overwhelmingly designed for the right hand. On the other hand, most male dogs have a strong tendency to be left-pawed, while the females have a weaker tendency to be right-pawed.

Different Strokes

Until the 1980s, it was wrongly thought that this 'lateralisation' of the body was something that happened only in human beings. In 1988, the eminent animal lateralisation researcher Charles R. Hamilton expressed everyone's amazement when he wrote: 'These results lead to the plausible but revolutionary inference that a bird more effectively searches for food with its right eye, while it watches for danger with its left!'

Since then, we have found evidence for lateralisation in most animals with spines, including reptiles, birds, fish, amphibians and yes, mammals — including dogs.

Which eye the animal uses to look at something affects how they learn, their spatial memory and their behaviour in avoiding threats.

In one study, pigeons were shown 725 abstract patterns. They could remember most of the patterns seen with their right eye (left brain), but did no better than chance with those seen by their left eye. Lateralisation begins at an early age. Bird embryos lie inside the shell, the right eye exposed to the light coming through the shell, while the left eye is blocked from the light by its own body.

It turns out that this specialisation, i.e. having specific functions located on one side or the other of the brain, has advantages. It makes you better at spotting a predator and quicker in responding.

Right Comes, Left Goes

It seems, roughly speaking, that the left brain is linked more to approaching something. The right brain is involved more in withdrawing, or moving away.

In general, it seems that the right brain (which controls the left side of the body) is more responsive to negative stimuli, and to oddities, emergencies and threats.

For example, birds tend to watch out for danger with their right brain (or left eye). Chicks leap away far more vigorously if they see danger with their left eye (as compared to their right eye) — and it's the same with toads. Chameleons will be much more aggressive if they see another chameleon with their left eye (as compared to the right eye). Chimpanzees experiencing negative emotions (e.g. a threat) will scratch the left side of the body more (controlled by the right brain).

However, the left brain (which controls the right side of the body) is more concerned with considered responses to routine situations.

And so birds, for example, tend to look for food with the right eye (or left brain). They tend to be better at using this eye to differentiate between various visual stimuli. Honeybees learn more readily if they use their right antenna (left brain). To scan for food, Australian kookaburras use the right eye (left brain) more. In human beings, the left brain seems to be more involved with love, bonding, attachment and safety.

Dogs Wag Tails

This brings us to the study undertaken by Dr Giorgio Vallortigara from the University of Trieste in Italy. He chose 30 domestic dogs (15 male and 15 female, aged 1–6 years) from the Obedience School at the Veterinary School of the University of Bari. He exposed these dogs to various situations, and made videos from above of how their tails responded.

The tail is a structure on the centre-line of the body, pulled on each side by muscles, which are in turn controlled by the left and right brain. Sometimes the different sides cooperate and sometimes they compete. This means that you should be easily able to identify any behaviour that tends to one side or the other.

When a dog saw its owner, its tail wagged on both sides of the centre line, but far more to the right than to the left. When the dog saw a random human being, the effect was not as pronounced, but still more to the right than to the left. However, when the dog saw a large, dominant unfamiliar dog, its tail wagged far more to the left than to the right.

It's quite easy to spot the effect if you look at a video of the dog's wagging tail shot from above, and even easier if it's slowed down. Unfortunately, in real-time, it's a subtle effect, and dogs wriggle around so much that the effect is hard to see with the untrained eye. But if you take the time to train your eye, you can spot the difference.

Now here's something to remember that may help you out. If the tail wags to the dog's right, then it's all right to pat, scratch or play catch with the dog. But if the tail wags to the dog's left, well it's best left to itself.

And here's the Take Home Message:

Tail to the right, it's all right,
Tail to the left, it's best you left.

References

Blakeslee, Sandra, 'Dog — happy or scared — appear to talk with their tails', *The New York Times*, 25 April 2007.

Quaranta1, A., Siniscalchi, M. and Vallortigara, G., 'Asymmetric tail-wagging responses by dogs to different emotive stimuli', *Current Biology*, 20 March 2007, pp R199–R201.

Rogers, Lesley J., 'Evolution of hemispheric specialization: Advantages and disadvantages', *Brain and Language*, 15 June 2000, Vol 73, No 2, pp 236–253.

Skiba, M., Diekamp, B., Prior, H. and Güntürkün, O., 'Lateralized interhemispheric transfer of color cues: Evidence for dynamic coding principles of visual lateralization in pigeons', *Brain and Language*, 15 June 2000, Vol 73, No 2, pp 254–273.

Vallortigara, Giorgio, 'Comparative neuropsychology of the dual brain: A stroll through animals' left and right perceptual worlds', *Brain and Language*, 15 June 2000, Vol 73, No 2, pp 189–219.

Peacock Plumage

In early 2008, I was invited to do a Triumphal Tour of India, speaking to the general public, as well as high schools and universities. There were the usual sightseeing opportunities and events — elephants, maidens throwing red rose petals in our path, the Taj Mahal, and peacocks. My primary school–aged daughter, Little Lola, accompanied me. She was so impressed that, on her return, she did a school project on the peacock. She made a magnificent model and wrote an essay that included the widely held belief that the purpose of the splendid plumage of the male (the peacock) is to attract the female (the peahen).

But this simple 'fact' is actually a puzzle, and is almost certainly wrong.

Cultural Peacock

The peacock is the National Bird of India — and since 1956, the symbol of the NBC TV network in the USA. It's also the logo of Sri Lanka Airlines.

And a peacock feather is always present in the crown of Lord Krishna, a deity in the Hindu faith.

Peacock 101

Strictly speaking, this bird is a 'peafowl', with a female 'peahen' and a male 'peacock'. But most of us call both genders a peacock.

There are two major species of peacock — the Blue or Indian Peacock (Pavo cristatus), found in India and Sri Lanka, and the Green or Javanese Peacock (Pavo muticus), which ranges from Burma to Java in Indonesia. In Africa there is also the Congo Peacock (Afropavo congensis), a species discovered as recently as 1936. Although a single feather of this bird was found in 1913, it took a further 23 years to locate the actual species.

Some 3,000 years ago, the Phoenicians carried the peacock to Egypt. The Romans raised peacocks to add a touch of class to their estates — and to eat.

Are you lookin' at me?

The peacock can raise the long feathers of the train into a glorious semicircle, about two metres across (not bad for a bird only about a metre long).

Each brilliant metallic green feather carries an iridescent 'eye'. The feathers keep growing during autumn and winter, and moult once each year in summer.

A male peacock

Peacock Throne

The Peacock Throne was one of the most magnificent imperial thrones ever built. It had silver steps and golden legs covered in jewels. Its back was a representation of two peacock trains and again was covered in precious stones.

It was built for the Mughal emperor Shah Janan in the 17th century. The Persian ruler Nader Shah captured Delhi in 1739 and seized the Peacock Throne. He took it back to Persia, but it was lost in wars with the Kurds, who broke it up for its precious parts.

Reproductions of the Peacock Throne were later made for subsequent shahs of Persia.

The peacock is 90–130 cm long and weighs about 5 kg, while the smaller peahen is about 86 cm long and weighs 3–4 kg.

Now the first thing to realise is that the peacock's 'tail' is not actually a 'tail'.

His real tail feathers are quite small and nondescript. The big showy feathers are actually the uppertail coverts on his back, and not part of his tail. To avoid confusion, bird scientists call it a 'train'. This train is so large that it is cumbersome when folded and can impede the peacock's pursuit of food or his escape from predators.

Peacock Evolution

It's all a fine balance.

Animals can evolve characteristics that are so exaggerated, that they can actually pose a danger to their survival. However, if this is offset by increased mating opportunities, then, on average, the animals with exaggerated characteristics might have more babies.

This is called the 'Condition-Dependent Theory of Sexual Advertisement'. It states that only males with superior genetic and physical condition can carry such a burdensome characteristic. Hopefully, in the fullness of time, the offspring will inherit this superior constitution, making them better able to find food, evade predators and impress members of the opposite gender.

This is the background to the belief that the peacock's magnificent feather display has evolved in order to attract the peahen.

Feather Colour

The colours in the feathers of the peacock do not come from dyes. Instead, they come from the regular geometric spacing of tiny cylinders of keratin.

The cylinders are formed into a square array with a spacing of about 150 nm (nanometres, or billionths of a metre). This gives (via some fancy physics, e.g. Bragg Reflection, Fabry–Perot Interference, etc.) a green colour. Blue comes with a spacing of 140 nm, while yellow has a spacing of 165 nm. (The combination of blue and yellow produces the illusion that we see as the colour green.)

This knowledge is being used in human-made optical devices. It is influencing the design of devices that help carry light down optic fibres, in order to carry massive amounts of information.

Peacock Display

The peacock can raise the long feathers of the train into a glorious semicircle, about 2 m in diameter (not bad for a bird that's only about a metre long). Each brilliant metallic-green feather carries an iridescent 'eye'. The feathers keep growing during autumn and winter and moult once each year in summer.

The story goes that when the peacock spies a potential mate, he erects the feathers in his train into a fan. He then draws the fan forward, wraps himself in it and sends ripples through the feathers. He then draws the fan further forward, quivering it so violently that the feathers make a rattling sound and appear to shimmer. This part of the courtship is called the 'ecstasy'.

The peacock will then manipulate the muscles at the bottom of each feather to change the loudness of the sound, and does this about twice each second. This is called a 'shiver'. A peacock keen to impress a peahen can generate up to 20 bouts of shivering, each bout lasting up to six minutes, or more.

The spectacular display is definitely performed for the benefit of the peahen. But she is not automatically won over. Instead, she will normally perform one of three behaviours — ignore it and pass on by, passively accept the display or actively solicit the display.

On the surface, this seems like a classic case of 'sexual advertisement' by the peacock. But over the years, there have been a few pieces of data that don't fit this simple picture.

We Have a Problem ...

First, the peacock often displays his train *after* the peahen has started the courtship ritual, not before. Surely, if the Big Display is his advertisement as to how good it can get, he should do a display *before* she starts the courtship.

Second, over the years, there has been conflicting evidence both for and against the link between the train display and the mating success by the peacock. However, a general consensus for this theory has not been reached.

Third, as a part of this conflict, there are still continuing arguments about what constitutes the most successful aspect of the train. Is it its length, the diameter of the eyes in the feathers, the number of eyes per square metre, the frequency of the shiver or the symmetry of the train? The question is far from resolved.

Fourth, the 'manufacture' of the train is controlled by oestrogen (female) hormones, which is very unusual for a display 'ornament' that supposedly affects mating success. Testosterone (male) hormones are far more common in this arena.

Fifth, there is actually not that much difference between the trains of peacocks across different populations of their species. So, to a potential mate, one peacock's plumage is as good as another's.

And finally, the 'quality' of the train itself does not accurately reflect the genetic and health conditions of the peacock — thus making it a false sexual advertisement.

So What's It For?

This leaves us with the increasingly probable position that the glorious train and display of the peacock is a 'signal' or advertisement that might have once had significance, but is now obsolete. In other words, the peahen is really interested in other aspects of the peacock (perhaps his stimulating conversation), but even to qualify in the mating stakes, he needs a pretty train.

To use mathematical language, perhaps the peacock train display is a necessary, but not sufficient, condition.

So why does he still have this glorious spread of plumage? Perhaps, like most male creatures, he's his own biggest fan …

References

Blau, Steven K., 'Light as a feather: Structural elements give peacock plumes their colour', *Physics Today*, January 2004, pp 18–20.

Encyclopædia Britannica, Ultimate Reference Suite DVD, 2006 — 'Peacock Throne'.

'Evolution: Vestigial finery', *Nature*, 17 April 2008, p 784.

Kodric-Brown, Astrid and Brown, James H., 'Why the fittest are the prettiest', *The Sciences*, September/October 1985, pp 26–33.

Takahashi, Mariko, et al., 'Peahens do not prefer peacocks with more elaborate trains', *Animal Behaviour*, 14 April 2008, Vol 75, pp 1209–1219.

Green Glow
of Radiation

We may not all be nuclear scientists, but there's one piece of nuclear knowledge that we all agree on — 'radioactivity has a green glow'. But regardless of what you see in *The Simpsons*, radioactivity does not glow green.

Cultural References to Glow

Most of us know the opening sequence of any episode of *The Simpsons*. Homer Simpson, my Personal Guru in all Matters Scientific, downs tools when the knocking-off bell rings at the nuclear power plant where he works. The radioactive material that he accidentally flips down the back of his shirt quite clearly has a green glow — luckily it's not reality TV.

Another fictitious character, Superman, can be brought to his knees only by kryptonite — which, you guessed it, has an unearthly glow. As the Superman character evolved, various shades of kryptonite appeared, but the commonest one has a green glow.

Many computer games show radiation-contaminated areas as having a green glow.

It's not easy glowing green

Say no to the glow

Even though radiation is universally thought of as having a green glow, our bodies simply do not have sensors that can detect alpha particles, beta particles, or gamma rays. Radioactivity is invisible to us — it's not green, or any other colour, it's totally invisible.

And even in the real world, hospital patients will laconically say that they've had so many X-rays that they glow in the dark. Indeed, the term 'glow in the dark' is a catch phrase for radioactivity.

Radioactivity

Although radioactivity has been around almost since the Big Bang, we only began to understand it in 1896. In that year, the French scientist Henri Becquerel discovered that uranium ores had the power to fog up photographic plates. The previously undiscovered radiation from the uranium was the fogging culprit.

In general, radioactivity occurs in atoms that are unstable. The core or nucleus of an unstable atom loses some energy, usually by squirting it out as either particles or radiation. The particles can be either alpha particles or beta particles, while the radiation is gamma radiation. Different types of radiation cause differing degrees of damage to the cells in living tissue.

Alpha particles can be stopped by a few centimetres of air, a sheet of paper, or even your skin. But if something that emits alpha particles bypasses the protective layer of your skin, gets inside your body and rests up against some cells, it can damage those cells. Beta particles have more penetrating power but can be stopped by only a thin sheet of aluminium. Gamma rays have the most penetrating power and can be stopped only by materials with greater density and/or thickness, such as concrete or lead.

Sensing Radiation

In general, we cannot sense radiation. But in conditions of extreme radiation, some of our other senses get overloaded and respond.

A very powerful solar storm hit the old Soviet/Russian space station *Mir* (a beautiful word for 'peace') while a Russian cosmonaut, Sergei Avdeyev, was inside. He 'felt' the radiation even though he had retreated to the internal safe room, which was partially screened by all the mass around it. He later said: 'I felt that the particles of radiation were walking through my eyes, floating through my brain, and maybe clashing with my nerves.'

No Sensors for Radioactivity

Now here is the core to busting the 'Green Glow of Radioactivity' myth. Our bodies simply do not have sensors that can detect alpha particles, beta particles or gamma rays. Radioactivity is invisible to us — it's not green, or any other colour, it's totally invisible.

This makes working with radioactive materials potentially dangerous, and it is the reason why very specific Occupational Health and Safety regulations have been set up for workers in the industry. They have to wear special Radiation Exposure Detection badges, precisely because radioactivity is invisible.

Glow-Boys or Jumpers

In the nuclear industry, especially in the USA, the terms 'glow-boy' or 'jumper' refer to temporary workers. They are called 'glow-boys' because they supposedly 'glow in the dark', and 'jumpers' because they jump into a highly radioactive environment, do one short job and then get out again.

In the 1970s, the glow-boy would carry out a high-risk repair or maintenance job in a very radioactive environment. Typically, these jobs consisted of cleaning up and removing radioactive waste, finding and repairing leaks, or doing emergency welding.

In one short job, they would be exposed to about ten times more radiation than the average member of the public would be in a whole year. A 'rem' is roughly the dose of radiation that you would get from 40 chest X-rays. In a few minutes, the jumpers would be exposed to about 5–12 rem of radiation.

Glow-boys were typically young men in their twenties. Unfortunately, they were not usually covered by either union protection or health insurance, and usually knew very little about the risks they were taking.

The statistics are very sketchy, but by 1976, jumpers were getting 47% of all the radiation received by all workers in the US nuclear industry. Because the money was good, some jumpers were working at five nuclear power plants in the same calendar year.

Chernobyl Glow-Boys

Many members of the Kruszelnicki family came from Lviv, a town in Ukraine. Over the centuries, the borders have shifted, and this city has had many names (including Lvov, Lviv and Lamberg), and many owners (e.g. Poland, Russia and Ukraine).

The family and I were wandering through a street market in Lviv one weekend, when I noticed a brightly coloured object. It was a medal with a scientifically correct depiction of how alpha particles, beta particles and gamma radiation would behave in an electrical field. My curiosity was piqued. The seller told me that this medal was given to the 'liquidators' of the nearby Chernobyl nuclear power plant.

On 26 April 1986, at 1.23 am (lots of bad things happen when people are tired), Reactor Number Four at the Chernobyl nuclear power plant near Pripyat in Ukraine exploded. It blew the 2,000-tonne lid off the reactor.

Inside the reactor building, the radiation levels were over 5 roentgen/sec — a lethal dose is 500 roentgen over five hours. The workers were receiving lethal doses within a few minutes — but didn't know it, because human beings don't have any sensors for radiation.

Soldiers, firefighters and workers (officially called 'liquidators', and unofficially called 'bio-robots' by the military) were sent into the reactor to clean up radioactive rubble and to do whatever was necessary to stop the situation from getting worse. In the following three months, 237 people suffered acute radiation sickness, 31 of them dying. Two decades after the disaster, the vehicles used by the liquidators are still parked in Chernobyl — and are still giving off 10–30 roentgen/hr.

I bought the brightly coloured medal in memory of those affected by the disaster.

Green-Glowing Radiation

But what about the green glow of the radium-painted wristwatches, night-time navigation instruments, pistol sights, external house numbers, internal light-switch panels in houses and even glowing eyes in toy dolls? Yes, from around 1913 to the 1960s, they did contain radium — and they did glow green.

But the radium itself does not give off a green glow.

Radium is extremely radioactive, being one million times more radioactive than uranium, weight for weight. There are approximately 25 isotopes, four of them existing in nature. The four natural isotopes have half-lives ranging from 3.6 days to 1,602 years.

The radium used in products like wristwatches etc. was mixed with a chemical called a phosphor (made from zinc sulphide mixed with either silver or copper). The radium gave off alpha particles, which hit the atoms in the phosphor. The alpha particles forced the electrons in these atoms to jump to a higher energy level. When the electrons fell back down to their original energy level, they gave off a greenish glow — hence the myth about anything radioactive having a green glow. But it was actually the phosphor *not* the radium that gave these old products a green glow.

Glowing Wristwatches

You can still buy glow-in-the-dark wristwatches today. But they don't have any radium in them.

They contain tritium — an unstable isotope of hydrogen, with a half-life of 12.3 years. It gives off low-energy beta particles, which hit a phosphor, which then glows. These are safe, as long as you don't break open the glass and try to eat or inhale the tritium. Tritium is also used in exit signs and on the sights of pistols and rifles.

Radium Girls

In the early part of the 20th century, there was the tragic case of the so-called Radium Girls.

The US Radium Corporation made paints that glowed green in the dark, which they sold under the name 'Undark'. The corporation also hired several hundred workers, all women, to paint highlights on about 250 watch dials each day. The women were paid about one-and-a-half cents per dial. They were encouraged to keep a fine point on their brushes by using their tongues or lips.

Once inside the body, radium behaves like calcium and goes to the bones. The Radium Girls all suffered horrible diseases from the radiation and died terrible deaths, and even today, some of their graves are radioactive. Five of these poor working-class women subsequently mounted a court case against the corporation.

As a result of the lengthy court case, safety standards for workers were vastly improved. The five Radium Girls each received US$10,000 in compensation.

Cherenkov Radiation

In some very uncommon cases, radioactive materials can also give off charged particles travelling at very high velocities. These particles can interact with the immediate environment to create a bluish glow. This environment can include the oxygen, nitrogen and water molecules in the air immediately around them, water in nuclear storage tanks, or water molecules that the radioactive materials absorb. This is called Cherenkov Radiation.

But, in general, don't think that you can recognise radioactivity by its green glow. That's about as 'see-through' as Little Green Men.

Sources of Light

There are many ways that we can generate light, other than by burning carbon or heating thin metal wires.

Chemiluminescence is used in so-called light sticks. A few chemicals combine to make a few other chemicals, and light is emitted. In a light stick, cyalume, water and a dye all combine to make a phenol, an activated dye, carbon dioxide and light.

Bioluminescence is a specific variety of chemiluminescence that uses the enzyme 'luciferase'. (Originally, Lucifer was God's favourite — indeed, his name means 'bringer of light'. But he displeased God and was cast out of Heaven into Hell.) This bioluminescence reaction is used by about 90% of the deep-sea life in the ocean to make light. This light is used for camouflage, attraction, repulsion and communication.

Electroluminescence occurs when an electric field acts on certain semiconductors to give light. It has industrial uses, because of the long life of the components (50 years or more) and low power consumption.

Mechanoluminescence occurs when mechanical energy somehow generates light. It has several varieties. One version, triboluminescence, was described back in 1620 by Francis Bacon. The mechanical energy forces electrical charges to separate and, eventually, make light. You can see this when you unpeel tape, open an envelope or crunch Life Savers lollies between your teeth in the dark.

Photoluminescence happens on a very short time scale. It takes about 10 billionths of a second for a photon of energy to land, and then be re-emitted as a photon of light. There are a few different varieties of photoluminescence. In 'phosphorescence', the physics involves 'forbidden' energy states — this gives a time delay of several hours. This is the phenomenon used by 'glow-in-the-dark' materials that can be recharged by exposing them to light. Another variety is 'fluorescence', named after calcium fluoride (as in the mineral, fluorite), in which it was first noticed. In this case, high-energy photons of ultraviolet light are absorbed and lower energy photons of visible light are emitted.

There are many other mechanisms by which light can be emitted, including radioluminescence, sonoluminescence and thermoluminescence.

Reference

Mackis, Roger M., 'The great radium scandal', *Scientific American*, August 1993, pp 94–99.

A Glass Act

If you enjoy reading Victorian novels, you'll probably come across the phrase 'ground glass'. Victorian authors had clever plots in which some of their fictional characters used this mysterious 'ground glass' to surreptitiously kill off unwanted relatives, in order to get their grubby little hands on the family fortune.

The 'ground glass kills you' myth persists to this day. For example, overenthusiastic, anti-drug lobbyists claim that unscrupulous manufacturers of ecstasy cut the drug with ground glass to make it doubly dangerous. (But wouldn't this immediately kill off their repeat business from returning customers?)

As usual, you can't believe everything you read and hear.

Glass 101

We have been making glass for over 3,500 years. The ancient Egyptians were making and exporting glass from their factories to their neighbours in Arabia, Mesopotamia, Syria, Cyprus and Crete around 1250 BC. Glass making was a complicated two-stage process. First, the raw materials were partially heated and then coloured and heated to a higher temperature to make round ingots that were exported to other workshops to be reworked into the final artefacts. At the time, the making of glass was a secret, guarded by the death penalty, and the glass itself was very precious and rare.

Glass was still precious and rare about 500 years ago. Back then, it was believed that if you ground up some glass and fed it to an enemy, it would kill them. A few centuries later, the slave chronicles of pre–Civil War America refer to disgruntled black slaves who 'poisoned masters and mistresses with arsenic, ground glass and "spiders beaten up in buttermilk"'.

In Victorian novels, the victim after ingesting the 'ground glass', would die slowly and very painfully, thereby giving the murderer much satisfaction. This method of killing also had the supposed advantage of being unknown to the medical profession. It was, therefore, supposedly undetectable, leaving the investigators completely baffled.

By the way, by 'ground glass' I don't mean a sheet of glass that has been ground to be flat, with a slightly rough (matte) finish. (This kind of glass is used in the focusing screens of expensive still and movie cameras.) No, I'm talking about the kind of glass that you get if you smash it up into tiny pieces. And you then maliciously mix it into someone's food.

Medical Studies

In 1642, the writer and physician, Sir Thomas Browne, described in his book, *Pseudodoxia Epidemica*, how he fed ground glass to dogs. He pointed out that at the time, it was commonly believed that ground glass added to the diet would kill. He explained how his test on the dogs had debunked the myth. (I guess he didn't have to deal with a Grants Committee or an Ethics Committee.) He wrote: 'That Glass is poison, according unto common conceit, I know not how to grant ... from experience, as having given unto

Can you stomach this?

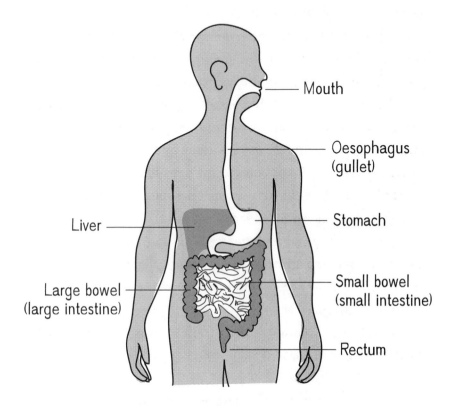

An internal look at our digestive tract

The gut is a very dynamic organ, continually writhing around
as it processes your food. It is also dynamic in itself — both
the wall thickness of the gut and the internal diameter of the
gut change all the time in a coordinated fashion.
It both grinds your food very finely, as well as pushing it
along the 8 metre-or-so length of the gut, before it finally
emerges into your toilet bowl.

Dogs above a dram thereof {of ground glass}, subtilly (sic) powdered in Butter and Paste, without any visible disturbance.'

It is possible to kill somebody with pieces of broken glass, but the circumstances have to be exceptional. In 1905, Dr F.J. Smith testified in court regarding the case of an infant who died this way. However, the infant had been force-fed 'a quantity of roughly powdered glass, a considerable amount of which was found after death in the stomach, which was coated with a thick layer of tenacious mucus streaked with blood'.

In 1916, Dr S.G. Shattock wrote a paper which examined the causes of appendicitis. He was especially interested in finding out whether swallowed items could cause appendicitis. He looked at iron filings, mine dust, steel fragments from grain-rolling mills, grape seeds, fragments of hair, sulphides of various metals including mercury and lead and, yes, broken or ground glass. He describes several experiments in which the feeding of ground glass had no ill effects — and he emphasised that 'if it is attended with a fatal result, this must be rare'.

Also in 1916, a poisoner in New York City testified that he had tried to use ground glass to kill people, but complained that it had proved useless.

Since then, many people have written about this supposed peril. However, the nicest summary probably comes from Dr D.P. Lyle who, in 2004, wrote the enticingly entitled *Forensics for Dummies*. In another of his books, published in 2003, *Murder and Mayhem: A Doctor Answers Medical and Forensic Questions for Mystery Writers*, he addresses the ground glass conundrum. He writes that 'very fine glass is unlikely to cause any lethal damage to the Gastro Intestinal tract ... Even with coarser glass, the bleeding would probably not be massive or life-threatening, but slow and (would) lead to anaemia and fatigue.'

True Now

In the TV series *Underbelly*, about the gangland wars in Melbourne in the late 1990s and early 2000s, Jason Moran bites off a chunk from a drinking glass to show his opponents how tough he is. It did him no harm. (It was a bit of lead that got him in the end!)

And what about all the magicians and performance artists who eat glass? They don't die from it. But, of course, all stage performances could be subject to trickery.

Which is why I was delighted to get an email from 'George'. He described his own personal experience of eating glass. He had seen other people do it, so he figured it was safe, if he was careful. He wrote: 'When I was young and therefore stupid enough, I had this party trick to amuse/amaze my friends. It was glass eating. And I am still alive. Strong young teeth are essential.

'After the first bite, which was quite tricky and could easily make your lip bleed (because no sticking out points and therefore no good grip; after the first piece is broken off — no problem), the rest was quite easy. You just broke piece by piece, crush it with your teeth and swallow. Pieces as big as your last finger bone (2 cm long approx.) go down no problems. I never had cuts/bleeding inside the mouth, or the other end — from the perspective of my now mature age, I must say — surprisingly!

'I usually proceeded till only the bottom piece — too thick to break with the teeth — was left.

'There were always wise guys who challenged me to eat that too, to which my response was "when you eat as much as I have, I will eat the bottom too, ha, ha, ha".

'I must stress; this is NOT hearsay. This is my personal experience.'

Physiology of Gut

The gut is a very dynamic organ, continually writhing around as it processes your food in the space between the bottom of your lungs and the top of your legs. The gut is also dynamic internally — both the wall thickness of the gut, and the internal diameter of the gut change continually in a coordinated fashion. These movements are generally called 'peristalsis'. So your gut both grinds your food very finely and pushes it along the 8-metre-or-so length of the gut, before it finally emerges into your toilet bowl.

Long, fat, sharp splinters of glass would definitely cause problems as they were shoved along your gut — but you would certainly notice such splinters as you chewed your meal.

And yes, chunks of jagged glass the size of match heads would cause bleeding as they rubbed against the soft interior of your gut. But with a chunk of glass in your mouth, you would certainly notice the unexpectedly rough texture of your meal.

You would even notice the glass if it were ground as finely as sand. (Ever had a picnic on a windy day at the beach?) And if the glass were ground so finely that you didn't notice its presence in your mouth, then neither would your gut.

It would seem that ground glass as a murder weapon would transparently reveal your murderous relative as a Pain in the Glass …

References

Barham, Andrea, *The Pedant's Revolt: Why Most Things You Think Are Right Are Wrong*, London: Michael O'Mara Books Limited, 2005, pp 22–23.

Jackson, Caroline M., 'Glassmaking in Bronze-Age Egypt', *Science*, 17 June 2005, Vol 308, No 5729, pp 1750–1752.

Lyle, D.P., *Murder and Mayhem: A Doctor Answers Medical and Forensic Questions for Mystery Writers*, New York: St Martin's Press, 2003.

Rehren, Thilo, et al., 'Late Bronze-Age glass production at Qantir-Piramesses, Egypt', *Science*, 17 June 2005, Vol 308, No 5729, pp 1756–1758.

Shattock, S.G., 'The Traumatic Causation of Appendicitis', The Proceedings of The Royal Society of Medicine, London, 1915–16, ix., Pathological Section, pp 26–27, 2 May 1916.

Smith, Dr F.J. (Editor), *Taylor's Principles and Practices of Medical Jurisprudence*, Fifth Edition, 1905, Vol ii, p 847.

Hyena Horribilis

Luckily we don't need to be zoologists to have three 'facts' about the Spotted Hyena (*Crocuta crocuta*) at our fingertips. One, they are some kind of dog. Two, they have the most powerful bite for their weight. And three, they are loathsome and cowardly scavengers.

These three 'facts' are wrong — but it gets even weirder. Not only does the female Spotted Hyena outrank the male, but she also has an organ that looks exactly like the male's penis. Even stranger, she gets pregnant and even gives birth through this organ.

Cats or Dogs?

First, hyenas are not members of the dog family. They are more closely related to cats.

Both cats and dogs are carnivorous mammals with spinal cords. They belong to the same Kingdom — Animalia; the same Phylum — Chordata (creatures with spinal cords); the same Class — Mammalia (which breast-feed their young); and the same Order — Carnivora (meat eaters).

However, about 50 million years ago, there was a parting of the ways — dogs splitting off along a pathway that led to the Family Canidae (which today includes dogs, wolves and foxes). The line

Hyena Horribilis
No real laughing matter

Hyenas are not, as commonly thought, a variety of dog.
They are actually closer to the cat family.

They live in Africa, the Middle East, Pakistan
and India.

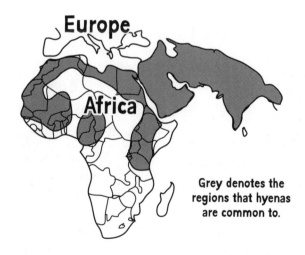

Grey denotes the
regions that hyenas
are common to.

that led to cats, mongooses and hyenas continued on into the Suborder Feliformia, which split and resplit over the next ten million years.

About 30 million years ago, hyenas split off along a pathway that led to the Family Hyaenidae. They flourished, and by 15 million years ago, there were at least 30 different species of hyena.

The Family of Hyaenidae then split off into various Subfamilies, two of which survive today — the Protelinae (the Aardwolf Hyena, 6–10 million years ago) and the Hyaeninae (which include Spotted, Striped and Brown Hyenas).

So the hyenas of today are very closely related to civets and mongooses, closely related to cats — and distantly related to the Canids (which include dogs, wolves and foxes).

Early Hyaenidae species did not have the bone-crushing molars of today's hyenas — they evolved into existence about 5–7 million years ago. The largest known hyena was the 200-kg *Pachycrocuta*. It lived from three million to half a million years ago and had massive teeth that could crush the bones of elephants.

Hyena Species

All hyena species tend to be nocturnal.

The Aardwolf Hyena (*Proteles cristatus*) (the name means 'earth wolf' in Afrikaans) looks like a small Striped Hyena. Its diet is so specialised that it will eat only two types of termites. Apart from the canines, its teeth have dwindled to mere pegs that can no longer chew meat. These solitary animals will lick up to 30,000 termites each night.

The Striped Hyena (*Hyena hyaene*) inhabits scrubland and arid and semiarid open country from Morocco to

Egypt and Tanzania in Africa. It is also found in Asia Minor, the Caucasus and India. It weighs 30–40 kg, has pale grey long hair with black fur on the throat, and stripes on the body and legs. The crest that runs from the ears to the tail is erectile. There is a three-month gestation period, the cubs being weaned at 10–12 months of age.

The Brown Hyena (*Hyaena brunnea*) is found in South Africa and along the western coastal deserts of Africa. It has pointed ears, a shaggy dark coat, with an erectile white mane over the neck and shoulders and horizontal white bands on the legs.

The gestation period is three months, weaning of the cubs occurring at 15 months. This species is smaller and lighter (40 kg) than the Spotted Hyena and inhabits much drier areas. These hyenas do not sniff each other's genitals as a greeting, but instead sniff heads, faces, necks and bodies.

The Spotted or Laughing Hyena (*Crocuta crocuta*) lives south of the Sahara, in rainforests, deserts, swamps and mountains and is the most numerous predator in the Serengeti. It is the largest hyena species — weighing up to 85 kg. The females are larger than the males, measuring up to 100 cm high at the shoulder and 2 m long, with a massive neck. They are also about 6.6 kg heavier. They have a ginger colour and a unique pattern of spots. Their 'laugh' is a signal of fear, excitement, or being chased. The gestation period is approximately four months, the young being weaned at 12–16 months, which is exceptionally late compared to other mammals.

Bite Club

Mentioning teeth brings us to the second myth about hyenas — that, weight for weight, they have the most powerful bite of any animal. A fascinating paper by Stephen Wroe from the University of Sydney, entitled 'Bite Club', compared the Bite Force Quotient of various animals (alive and extinct, mammal and marsupial), as it related to their body weight. It was higher in marsupials and in animals that consistently attacked animals larger than themselves. The Spotted Hyena came in at 117 — only slightly ahead of the lion at 112, but behind the tiger (127), the African Hunting Dog (142) and well behind the Tasmanian Devil at 181. The all-time winner was the Australian Marsupial Lion at 196.

By the way, while the favourite food of Spotted Hyenas seems to be zebra, they will eat anything.

On one hand, a pack of hyenas will entirely devour a 180-kg zebra in less than 25 minutes, leaving behind only bloodstained earth. They will later vomit up the hooves and the hair. In another example of Big Eating, a pack of 35 hyenas ate an adult zebra and her two-year-old foal (with an estimated total weight of 350 kg) in less than 30 minutes. A single Spotted Hyena can eat over 18 kg at a single meal — more than one-third of its weight. It is one of the very few animals that can eat every part of a carcass, including the bones. (In fact, their droppings are often white and crusty, thanks to the amount of bone in their diet.) This may explain why they are associated with gluttony, uncleanliness and even cowardice.

On the other hand, Spotted Hyenas will also happily eat rotten meat that would make other animals quite sick. Scientists are studying the immune system of the Spotted Hyena to try to work out why they are unaffected by eating tainted flesh, and why they do not seem to suffer from any major infectious diseases.

Scavenger

As mentioned, hyenas will sometimes eat meat that has been hanging around for so long that it has gone rotten. Doesn't this surely mean that they are scavengers?

After all, in the Disney movie *The Lion King* they are described as 'slobbery, mangy, stupid poachers', while Ernest Hemingway saw them as a 'devourer of the dead ... sad yowler, camp-follower, stinking, foul'. The *Encyclopaedia Britannica* acknowledges this common belief with, 'The Spotted Hyena, widely known as a scavenger, has heavy jaws equipped for crunching bones.'

So let's look at this so-called scavenging behaviour.

For one thing, no sensible carnivore is going to let a perfectly good meal of edible meat go to waste. After all, they don't even have to expend energy to chase it — it's just lying there for the taking. So tigers, lions, cheetahs, jaguars and yes, hyenas, will all eat carrion.

In addition, the noted wildlife biologist George Schaller, after several decades of observing these animals, claimed that lions scavenged more kills than Spotted Hyenas. And zoologist Dr Kay Holekamp, who has been studying Spotted Hyenas for a few decades, agreed, saying 'it is far more frequent that the lion will steal a kill from the hyenas' than vice versa.

She also noted that hyenas are excellent hunters, catching about 95% of what they eat.

So if lions aren't accused of being scavengers, why accuse hyenas?

Spotted Hyena 101

Spotted Hyenas have long legs, and a powerful neck, jaw and shoulders for carrying and ripping apart their prey. They are tireless trotters and have been observed travelling at 60 kph for 3 km.

The naturalist, Hans Kruuk, spent three and a half years observing the Spotted Hyenas of the Serengeti. He was impressed by these sophisticated hunters living in complex clans — he had originally expected to find solitary scavengers.

Spotted Hyenas live in clans of up to 80 members, but beyond this, they split into smaller groups. They live in communal dens — a collection of underground tunnels with many above-ground entrances. They come together only for three occasions — kills, defending their territory and socialising at the communal den. Their territory ranges from 40 to 1,000 km^2.

They are very intelligent — possibly as smart as primates. When zoologists put a hyena into a small metal cage with a latch, the animal quickly learnt how to flip open the latch.

Like primates, they have a high social intelligence and learn and follow the relevant rules of their society, form temporary and permanent coalitions within their clans and can understand the importance of some relationships over others.

They can solve social problems using sophisticated mechanisms, such as conciliation, distraction and even deception. For example, a hungry, low-ranking hyena might give the Alarm

Cry while higher-ranking members of the clan are feeding. When the other hyenas leave the area to respond to the nonexistent danger, the low-ranking hyena moves in to eat its fill.

Confused Sexuality — History

It's been known for a long time that there was something special about the sexual anatomy and physiology of the Spotted Hyena.

Quite a few ancient writers declared that the Spotted Hyena was a hermaphrodite with the genitals of both sexes in one body, or that it could change its sex. The Greek philosopher Aristotle (384–322 BC) mentions these claims but says that they are untrue. The Roman poet Ovid (43 BC–17 AD), who was famous for his love poems, thought that the hyena could change its gender. A few centuries later, the great Roman thinker and scientist Pliny the Elder (23–79 AD) also refers to Aristotle's claims. St Clement of Alexandria (c. 150–211/216 AD) wrote in his *Paedogogus* that the hyena was 'quite obsessed with sexual intercourse'. He believed that male hyenas could have sex with each other. But the Roman writer Claudius Aelianus (c. 175–c. 235 AD) preferred the hermaphrodite theory, claiming that the Spotted Hyena could change its sex in alternate years.

Quite frankly, there was very little real knowledge about this species until the autumn of 1935, when the zoologist L. Harrison Matthews chartered a truck at Arusha, in Tanganyika Territory in East Africa.

He set off on safari, killing about 103 Spotted Hyenas either with poisoned baits or bullets. He dissected them as soon as he could after they died. He examined them closely in the field, and then stored their genital tracts for later re-examination in England. He finally wrote up his results in 1939.

Confused Sexuality — Anatomy

According to Harrison Matthews the females are truly astonishing. They have a clitoris that looks just like a penis, and through which they give birth! The technical term for this is 'extreme masculinisation of the external genitalia'.

The clitoris is so enlarged that it looks just like the male hyena's penis — zoologists call it a 'pseudopenis' or a 'peniform clitoris'. It even has a narrow channel running through it to the outside world. Like the male hyena's penis, the pseudopenis has two 'corpora cavernosa' and a single 'corpus spongiosum'. This means that the female Spotted Hyena could have a genuine erection of its pseudopenis, as does the male with his penis. The clitoris is also as long as the male's penis — about 17 cm.

The female's labia are fused together, and because it has two fatty pads, it looks almost identical to a male's scrotum.

So thanks to the pseudopenis and the fused swollen labia, sometimes even hyena specialists cannot tell the difference between boy and girl hyenas. On a few occasions, Dr Holekamp was surprised when a 'male' she had known since birth suddenly delivered cubs, proving that 'he' was actually a 'she'. Perhaps this is how the misinformation about Spotted Hyenas being hermaphrodites came about.

Female Spotted Hyenas do have a vagina, but it does not open directly to the outside world. Instead, it communicates with the outside world via the pseudopenis. It is a true vagina both in its appearance to the naked eye — and under a microscope.

Only Spotted Hyena females have the pseudopenis. The females of other hyena species have 'regular' female genitals.

Confused Sexuality — Physiology

Female Spotted Hyenas urinate, copulate and give birth through the pseudopenis.

Mating is impossible without the full cooperation of the female. The male has to balance himself very precariously, because of the orientation of the pseudopenis.

The reproductive tract runs from the vagina, past the opening of the bladder and through the pseudopenis to the outside world. This means that the sperm have a long way to travel. Thanks to the position of the urinary bladder, she can flush out the sperm, if she changes her mind after mating.

The reproductive tract has a hairpin turn along its length, as well as a small opening to the outside world. This means that it's hard to give birth. Indeed, according to Harrison Matthews 'lacerations to the margin of the opening are not uncommon'. Birth is a very uncomfortable process that kills one in ten mothers, and suffocates 60% of the first-born cubs.

Hyena Cubs

The pregnant Spotted Hyena goes off by herself to give birth. When the cubs are one month of age, she moves them back to the communal den, where they stay for eight months. She has only two nipples, so if she has three cubs, the least aggressive one will starve.

The cubs have only their mother's milk for the first six months. Meat is then added to the diet until they are weaned at 12–16 months of age. By this time, they have a full set of adult teeth. But because their massive jaws and skulls take a few more years to mature, the mother must take care of them for 2–4 years. The mothers are very caring, tolerant and affectionate.

Hyena in Human Society

In Africa, the hyena was associated with divination, and thought of as a tool of demons and witches, much like the black cat in medieval European society.

Witches and sorcerers were thought to travel either by riding on its back, or by turning into a hyena.

It was also believed that the 'laughter' of the Spotted Hyena could not only closely imitate the human voice, but could also call the potential victims individually by name.

Even though the Masai of Africa traditionally despise the hyena, they will leave out their dead for the hyenas to eat.

Hyena Society — Women First

There are very few female-dominated societies.

Spotted Hyenas live in such a society. The lowest status female outranks the highest status male. The females are more aggressive than the males.

The female cubs inherit the status of their mother — thanks to male hormones. High-status female cubs are much larger, heavier and stronger than low-status female cubs. This begins before birth, with the high-ranking mother bathing her unborn cubs in the higher levels of male androgen hormones excreted from her ovaries. (The levels of male hormones are not as high in the low-ranking pregnant mothers.) These hormones make them bigger and stronger. Indeed, during the second half of pregnancy, the male hormone levels are higher in these pregnant females than they are in the males!

The high-ranking female cubs are off to a golden start in life — first access to the food, as well as more powerful allies and a better grade of protection. As a result, she has a longer reproductive life and more litters. Her teeth are in better condition, because she doesn't have to crush bones which can damage them. Instead, she can feast on the best and most tender meat. Alpha females are younger when they first get pregnant, mate more frequently, have cubs more often, and their cubs have a greater survival rate. Even so, all the females have cubs, because they can also pick and choose from the low-ranking males.

They avoid incest with this simple rule — a female will mate only with males who arrived after she was born. (In other words, she prefers to have sex with strangers.) Indeed, only 11% of males mate within the clan in which they were born. About 89% of males leave the clan when they become sexually mature, around the age of two or three. They then have to spend two years as a junior male, with no matings during this period. They are the very lowest ranking animal in the clan, being bossed around by all the other males and females, and having the very last access to the food and the females. It's a very hard life being a male Spotted Hyena.

When two Spotted Hyenas meet, they carry out a complex ritualised one-on-one ceremonial sniffing of the genitals, the submissive animal initiating the greeting. It lifts a hind leg to expose its erect pseudopenis or penis, for the more dominant hyena to sniff. Hyenas have anal glands that secrete a yellow oily substance, which they scrape onto grass or bushes to mark their territory. In the greeting ceremony, they will turn this gland inside out, in order to give the other hyena a better sniff. It sure is cheaper than Chanel No. 5!

Bad Rep

Spotted Hyenas are not solitary, skulking, cringing cowards, nor are they scavengers. Instead, they are sophisticated and skilled hunters that live in a complex society. The doting mothers probably invest more time and energy in raising their young than any other animal.

Unfortunately, Spotted Hyenas have such an undeservedly bad reputation that zoos don't want to exhibit them, and conservation groups don't want to adopt them. (Have you seen a hyena on a conservation T-shirt recently?)

So we don't get to see them at close quarters and learn the real facts about these amazing Gender-Bending, Role-Reversing animals.

References

Dloniak, S.M., et al., 'Rank-related maternal effects of androgens on behaviour in wild Spotted Hyenas', *Nature*, 27 April 2006, pp 1190–1193.

Encyclopædia Britannica, Ultimate Reference Suite DVD, 2006 — 'hyena'.

Encyclopædia Britannica, Ultimate Reference Suite DVD, 2006 — 'scavenger'.

Harrison Matthews, L., 'Reproduction in the Spotted Hyena, *Crocuta crocuta* (Erxleben)', Philosophical Transactions of The Royal Society of London, Series B, Biological Sciences, Vol 230, No 565, 5 July 1939, pp 1–78.

Höner, O.P., et al., 'Female mate-choice drives the evolution of male-biased dispersal in a social animal', *Nature*, 16 August 2007, pp 798–801.

Kemper, Steve, 'Who's laughing now?', *Smithsonian* magazine, May 2008, pp 76–84.

Lloyd, John and Mitchinson, John, *QI: The Book of Animal Ignorance*, London: Faber and Faber, 2007, pp 102, 103.

Wroe, Stephen, et al., 'Bite club: Comparative bite force in big biting mammals and the prediction of predatory behaviour in fossil taxa', Proceedings of The Royal Society of London, Series B, Vol 272, 22 March 2005, pp 619–625.

Hooked on Hookah

For centuries people in Eastern countries have been using the hookah, or Indian water pipe. And recently, it has been gaining renewed popularity in its traditional territories, as well as picking up additional adherents in Europe and the USA. This is happening because people believe that bubbling tobacco smoke through water makes it 'safe' — but this claim is false.

Tobacco — The Numbers

Worldwide, tobacco kills about 5.4 million people each year. Trends in smoking vary across the world.

In the USA, the smoking rate has dropped by almost half over the past four decades, from 42% of adult Americans smoking in 1965 down to 22% in 2003. For this reason, tobacco companies are redirecting their marketing.

Smoking a hookah was almost unknown in Europe and the USA in 1990, but things have changed. By early 2006, there were over a thousand hookah lounges and cafés in the USA. A 2008 survey at Virginia Commonwealth University showed that 50% of first-year students had used a hookah at least once, and 20% had used one in the previous month.

Hookah smoking has always been popular among adult males

in the Eastern Mediterranean Region (EMR), but recently women and young people have taken up the hookah in enormous numbers. In 2007, the Global Youth Tobacco Survey looked at over 90,000 students aged 13–15 in the EMR. They found that, while 6.7% of boys and 3.2% of girls smoked cigarettes, the figures were much higher for other forms of tobacco smoking (mostly hookahs) at 15.6% of boys and 9.9% of girls.

A recent study of Lebanese school children (average age 15 years) showed that 51% currently used tobacco — 25% used the hookah exclusively, 20% used cigarettes exclusively and 6% used both.

A survey of female university students in Cairo in Egypt asked why they smoked the hookah. Of those surveyed, 74% believed that hookahs caused significantly less harm than cigarettes.

However, it's surprisingly easy for susceptible people to become addicted. Several large surveys of adolescents have shown that some people become addicted after just one cigarette.

Hookah History

Apparently, the hookah was first used in the 14th century. It was probably reinvented in India at least four centuries ago, and shortly afterwards spread into the Middle East and the Mediterranean region. One legend claims that it was invented by the physician, Hakim Abul Fath, for the Indian Emperor Akbar (who ruled between 1556 and 1605) so that tobacco 'smoke should be first passed through a small receptacle of water so that it would be rendered harmless'.

So even back then, it was wrongly believed that filtering tobacco smoke through water made it 'safe'.

The hookah (its Indian name) is called the *narghile* in eastern Mediterranean countries including Syria and Turkey, and *goza* and *shisha* in some northern African countries and Egypt. In Western

Hookah Anatomy 101

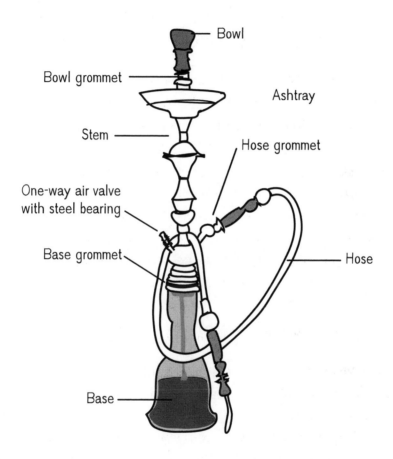

Bowl

Bowl grommet

Ashtray

Stem

Hose grommet

One-way air valve
with steel bearing

Base grommet

Hose

Base

The commonly used Hookah, or Indian water pipe

The designs may vary slightly, but they always have
the smoke passing through water.
The stuff that is smoked is not some exotic
unknown-to-Western-medicine 'safe' vegetable matter
— it's regular tobacco, with or without flavouring.

society, it's also known as a 'hubble-bubble' or a 'water pipe' — although it's different from a 'bong', a water pipe used for smoking grass.

Hookah 101

The designs vary slightly, but hookahs always have the common feature of smoke passing through water.

The stuff that is smoked is not some exotic unknown-to-Western-medicine 'safe' vegetable matter — it's regular tobacco, with or without flavouring. It comes in three main preparations.

'Tobamel' (derived from the words 'tobacco' and 'mel' meaning 'sweet' or 'honey') is a mix of tobacco and molasses and/or honey. However, to jazz it up, the tobacco can be moistened with water, and/or enhanced with fruit flavours. The fruit flavours can include virtually anything, e.g. pomegranate juice, rose oil, sour cherries or grapes. Tobamel is more popular with young urban women.

'Tumbak' is just a variety of tobacco, that has been washed and dried a few times.

Finally, there's 'jurak', which is halfway between tobamel and tumbak. Typically, it's sweetened, but not flavoured — but sometimes, it's the opposite.

The tobacco (yep, the stuff that slows you down, wrecks your lungs and gives you lung cancer and heart disease) sits in a small bowl right at the top of the hookah. It is heated by placing a burning coal just above it — in the good old days a glowing coal from a convenient brazier or firebox and, today, a convenient 'quick-igniting' charcoal. The smoke then heads down through a stem, the bottom of which is submerged about 2–3 cm in a bowl of water (say half a litre). The smoke then bubbles up through the water into an open chamber, from which it is drawn into a pipe (say 1.5 m long). It's all powered by the human being sucking on the end of it. The tobacco in the bowl is continually replenished during a smoking session.

Hookah Maintenance

Some hookah sales shops offer advice on how to keep your hookah in good condition.

This is what one website says about the hose that runs from the water bowl (where all the 'bad guys' are supposedly taken out) to your mouth:

'b. After 30 or so uses the inner lining of the hose as well as the inside of the wooden ends starts to wear down and deteriorate.

c. You should change your hose anywhere between your 30th–50th smoking session, depending on how long your average smoking session lasts.'

Now this seems odd. If the water takes out the bad chemicals, why should the inner lining of the hose and the inside of the wooden ends deteriorate? This implies that the bad chemicals are getting through the water and attacking the rubber hose and the wooden ends. If they can attack the rubber, what are they doing to the airways and lungs of the hookah smokers?

If only smokers could exchange their airways, lungs and heart after every 30–50 smoking sessions!

Hookah Safe for Tobacco?!

Some tobaccos meant for use in hookahs are advertised as containing 0% tar. One popular water-pipe tobacco sold in the USA and southwest Asia claims that it contains '0.5% nicotine and

0% tar'. This is very true, but totally misleading. All tobaccos contain 0% tar to start with — the tar is generated as a product of combustion only when the tobacco is heated.

When tobacco is burnt, two types of products are produced — gases and particles. The gases include nitrogen and carbon dioxide (which are harmless) and nasties such as carbon monoxide, nitrosamines, acetaldehyde, formaldehyde, hydrogen cyanide and various volatile hydrocarbons. The particles include aerosols of tar and nicotine particles (also nasty).

People assume that hookah smoke is safe because they believe that the water absorbs all the nasty chemicals and magically lets the 'good' chemicals through. This is *false*.

In the case of nicotine, most of it is left in the water, but some still gets into the lungs and, 11 seconds later, into the brain. So hookah smokers do exactly what regular cigarette smokers do with low nicotine cigarettes — they suck harder to get the nicotine hit. With the increased volume of smoke comes more of all the other nasties — carbon monoxide, heavy metals, hydrogen cyanide and a whole bundle of potent carcinogens.

Hookah Smokers Puff Up

Hookah smokers suck harder, and deeper — and more often. As a result, they suck in 50–100 times more smoke than a cigarette smoker.

A cigarette takes about 5–7 minutes to smoke. During this time, the smoker will suck in some 8–12 puffs, typically with a volume of 40–75 ml. So they'll suck in a total of about half to three-quarters of a litre of tobacco smoke.

But a water-pipe session typically lasts 20–80 minutes. The smoker will take approximately 50–200 puffs, each of which has a volume of 0.15–1 litre. Therefore, during a typical session a hookah smoker will inhale about 50 litres of smoke.

So in a hookah session, the smokers get about 1.7 times as much nicotine as they do from a single cigarette. But to get the nicotine, they have to inhale a huge volume of smoke. Unfortunately, this gives them 36 times more carcinogenic tar than a cigarette, as well as 15 times more carbon monoxide.

Cigarette vs Hookah

The experiences of cigarette smokers and hookah smokers are very different.

Cigarette smokers smoke more frequently but for much shorter periods. They see smoking as a mundane, oppressive personal addiction (which for some males was part of becoming a 'real man'), while hookah smokers see the experience as a pleasurable social one, involving togetherness and cultural identity. Cigarette smokers feel ostracised, while hookah smokers feel socially accepted.

Cigarette smokers usually start smoking as teenagers, while hookah smokers start in their twenties.

Cigarette smokers do (correctly) realise that smoking is bad for their health. But hookah smokers have the false belief that their smoking is relatively harmless both to themselves and to others around them.

Finally, many cigarette smokers do so to relieve stress, while hookah smokers see it as entertainment, a leisure pursuit and an escape.

Hookah Not Safe

Sadly, the result is not surprising. Hookah smokers are five times more likely to suffer from lung cancer and gum disease, when compared to non-smokers.

Hookahs are not a safe alternative to cigarettes. You can also catch or transmit infectious diseases by the sharing of the water pipe, e.g. tuberculosis and hepatitis. The heat sources (especially the quick-igniting charcoals) used to ignite the tobacco also add extra health risks, thanks to their own toxicants, metals and cancer-causing chemicals. And don't forget the second-hand smoke circulating in the room.

Hookahs are gaining in popularity. This could be due to their novelty value, their association with the mystique of the mysterious East or their pleasant flavours.

However, the safety claims are just a puff of hot air. After all, where there's smoke, there's fire.

References

Al-Mutairi, Sana S., et al., 'Comparative analysis of the effects of hubble-bubble (Sheesha) and cigarette smoking on respiratory and metabolic parameters in hubble-bubble and cigarette smokers', *Respirology*, July 2006, Vol 11, Issue 4, pp 449–455.

Eissenberg, Thomas, et al., 'Waterpipe tobacco smoking on a U.S. college campus: Prevalence and correlates', *Journal of Adolescent Health*, May 2008, Vol 42, Issue 5, pp 526–529.

Klein, Jonathan D., 'Hookahs and waterpipes: Cultural tradition or addictive trap?', Editorial, *Journal of Adolescent Health*, May 2008, Vol 42, Issue 5, pp 434–435.

O'Connor, Anahad, 'The claim: Hookahs are safer than cigarettes', *The New York Times*, 11 September 2007.

World Health Organization, 'Advisory Note: Waterpipe Tobacco Smoking: Health Effects, Research Needs and Recommended Actions by Regulators', WHO Study Group on Tobacco Product Regulation (ISBN 92 4 159385 7), 2005.

Maritime Marriage

Marriage has been around for thousands of years, in virtually every society, past or present. Ships have been sailing the oceans for a long time too. In the past, journeys at sea could last months or years. Perhaps this is why people have come to believe that a ship's captain has the power to perform marriages. However, apart from a few very recent examples, this is a myth.

History of Marriage

Every society has some kind of marriage ceremony — authorised and/or recognised by state, religion or society.

Sometimes, the religious authority acts as an agent of the state, automatically making the religious marriage legal. Sometimes, there has to be a separate state ceremony after the religious ceremony and sometimes, merely living together as husband and wife automatically 'marries' the partners under common law. In some countries the ceremony can be held just about anywhere, and in other countries it can only be held in a specific location (e.g. a church or a registry office).

As part of the process the partners to the marriage have certain rights and duties, usually with some mention of the offspring. Depending on the society, there can be many rules. Sometimes, one has to marry someone who is part of the tribe or group (endogamy), or sometimes, someone from outside the tribe or group (exogamy).

Marriage 101

The most common marriage is the one man/one woman partnership, but there are alternatives.

In modern times, the first country to legalise same-sex marriages was the Netherlands, in 2001. Today, some six countries allow same-sex marriages. The first recorded same-sex marriage was by the Roman poet Juvenal, in his second *Satire*, early in the 2nd century AD.

There also exists a practice where one person has two or more spouses at the same time. The more common version of this is called polygamy (one man with several wives), while less common is polyandry (one woman with several husbands).

A very uncommon practice is the Group Marriage, where several men marry several women.

Exchange marriages are more common. For example, among some Australian Aborigines, the ideal marriage has two men from different communities marrying each other's sister.

Tree marriages, once quite common in India, had a number of versions. In one version a conventional male/female marriage occurred near or on a tree. The tree supposedly had sacred or mystic powers (healing, fertility, etc.) that would flow on to the couple to benefit their future lives together. Another version recognised the special powers of the tree, a person marrying the tree in a symbolic marriage. Another version was a 'proxy' marriage. In some parts of India, a man could not marry a widow unless he was a widower. So the way to 'work around' the problem was to have him 'marry' a tree that was immediately chopped down, making him a 'widower'. This gave him the appropriate status needed to marry a widow.

Can't Marry at Sea

But ships' captains have never — until very recently — performed marriages.

In fact, both the US and UK governments have specific regulations for the captains of military and civilian ships. They are clearly forbidden to perform marriage ceremonies and do not, and never have had, the authority to do so. Here is a direct quote from the US Navy *Code of Federal Regulations*, Title 32, Subtitle A, Chapter VI, Subchapter A, Part 700, Subpart G, Rule 716, also known as 32 CFR 700.716): 'The commanding officer shall not perform a marriage ceremony on board his ship or aircraft. He shall not permit a marriage ceremony to be performed on board when the ship or aircraft is outside the territory of the United States, except: (a) In accordance with local laws ... and (b) In the presence of a diplomatic or consular official of the United States.'

But today there are a few exceptions.

Can Marry at Sea

Captains of Japanese ships can now perform marriage ceremonies, but only for those who hold Japanese passports.

Since 1998, a few cruise lines have offered wedding packages — perhaps to gain extra revenue, or perhaps from a deep and profound respect for the sacrament of marriage.

Ships' captains (until recently) never performed marriages

It seems that people possibly were confused with the huge amount of power and authority a ship's captain had ... and simply thought that this power included the power to perform marriages.

The Love Boat

Just Married

The captains of Cruise West ships can obtain a temporary permit to perform marriages — but only in certain Alaskan waters, including Prince William Sound, LeConte Glacier and Misty Fjords. However, prior to the ceremony, arrangements have to be made with the countries that abut these waters. After the marriage ceremony, the captain then has to mail the licence to the relevant courthouse, so that the marriage can be legally registered.

It is also possible to get married at sea on a few of the Princess Line ships. These ships (*Gold Princess, Grand Princess* and *Star*

Princess) are registered in Bermuda, and the captains have Burmuda licences to perform marriages, but only while the ships are in international waters. The price ranges from $1,000 to as much as you wish to pay. The Princess 'Tie the Knot at Sea' Wedding Program can include a live string quartet, champagne, a three-tiered wedding cake, both still and movie photography, flowers, wedding-cam so that your relatives across the world can watch the ceremony on the internet as it happens and, of course, the captain in a sparkling white uniform performing the ceremony.

You can also get married when the ship pulls into a port, if you have previously done all the paperwork for that particular country. In this case, the ceremony can take place on land ('Tie the Knot Ashore'), or on the ship ('Tie the Knot Harborside'). If it takes place onboard, it would be highly unlikely for the captain to perform the ceremony. They would rarely have authority to do so. Instead, you would have to organise a celebrant recognised by the country concerned.

So Why?

In the academic land of folklore research, no-one has been able to track down exactly how this myth started. However, the captain of a ship has a huge amount of authority and power, and I guess that people have just assumed that this power included the power to perform marriages.

Or perhaps the people who started the myth were all at sea.

We Wanted to Get Married on a Ship

In 2006, Mary and I got married on the Longest Day of the Year, when the Midnight Sun does not set on Norway. There was a lot of travelling involved. Three generations of the family flew for 36 hours in one continuous run of flights to get to Kirkenes in Norway, deep inside the Arctic Circle. (Kirkenes is a long way from most places, especially Sydney.) The plan was to then experience the Midnight Sun for seven days as the big cruise ship took the Honeymoon Couple (plus the kids and grandparents) down the coast to the southern end of Norway.

After being mostly awake for 36 hours, we landed, quite jet-lagged, in Kirkenes. We slept, woke up the next morning, had breakfast, and then drove for a few hours in a mud-splattered purple truck to get married in a mist-enshrouded church on the Russian border. My youngest child, Lola, was deeply disappointed that the purple truck was not a proper wedding car with ribbons.

The original plan had been to get a ship's captain to marry us, as we floated down the Norwegian coast on a cruise ship.

But we could only get married on land. So we had to jump through many hoops with various government departments in Australia and Norway to get the paperwork signed. Then we ran into trouble with the Norwegian Q150 and Q151 forms.

They were almost identical to the Q268 and Q269 forms, which was very confusing. Which ones to use? It took quite a few international phone calls to various Norwegian authorities to clear this up.

Finally, the man on the phone started asking the right questions. 'Now, Karl, are you a man?' 'Yes,' I replied, a little surprised. And then he asked, 'And this person you wish to marry, this Mary, is that person a man or a woman?' 'A woman,' I replied, even more surprised. Once he realised that we were man and woman, he said, 'Ah, then you want the heterosexual marriage, not the homosexual marriage, so you should fill out the Q150 and Q151.'

This didn't seem so odd when we realised that Norway allows same-sex marriages. As a result, a significant number of the foreign wedding planners who contact the Norwegian authorities would be more interested in the legal same-sex wedding that they could not get in their own countries.

References

Encyclopædia Britannica, Ultimate Reference Suite DVD, 2006 — 'marriage'.

Green, Joey, *Contrary to Popular Belief: More than 250 False Facts Revealed*, New York: Random House, 2005, p 185.

Richlin, Amy, 'Not before homosexuality: The materiality of the Cinaedus and the Roman law against love between men', *Journal of the History of Sexuality*, 1993, Vol 3, Issue 4, pp 523–573.

Varasdi, J Allen, *Myth Information: More Than 590 Popular Misconceptions, Fallacies, and Misbeliefs Explained!*, New York: Random House, 1996, pp 49, 50.

Fraudulent Flipper

Dolphins get amazingly good press — even the *Encyclopaedia Britannica* tells us that they are 'noted for their friendliness to humans'. They have enjoyed nothing but good PR over the past few thousand years. But don't believe it — dolphins are just wild animals, albeit with a cute smile. In fact, their permanent, fixed smile is not an indication that they love us — it's just a happy accident caused by the curve of their mouth.

Dolphins Love Us

Dolphins have been around for about 20 million years. In ancient Greek the name means 'fish with a womb'. So even back then, the Greeks realised that dolphins were different from the other fish in the ocean.

The ancient Greeks also thought that having a dolphin ride the bow wave or wake of your ship meant good luck.

Overall, dolphins are perceived as creatures of universal love and goodwill, intent on spreading peace on Earth. Some people perceive the naïve innocent dolphins as inferior to us, in need of our love, help and protection to survive. Others think that dolphins are our equals, with similar intelligence and language. And some people see dolphins as our superiors in all things except the ability to handle tools — a kind of benevolent, smiling, extraterrestrial genius with fins and no hands. These preconceptions never involve the slightest hint of aggression.

You Can't Trust TV

Over half of these false impressions about dolphins come from TV, books, aquariums and schools, with music trailing slightly behind. The original TV series *Flipper*, and its later franchised versions, have to take a lot of the blame. The *Flipper* theme song ran:

> *They call him Flipper, Flipper, faster than lightning.*
> *No one, you see, is smarter than he.*
> *And we know Flipper, lives in a world full of wonder,*
> *Flying there under, under the sea!*
> *Everyone loves the king of the sea,*
> *Ever so kind and gentle is he.*
> *Tricks he will do when children appear,*
> *And how they laugh when he is near!*
> **(Henry Vars and William D 'By' Dunham, 1963)**

The countercultural author J.C. Lilly took a pseudoscientific approach. He helped spread totally unrealistic notions about dolphins with his two books *Man and Dolphin* (1962) and *The Mind of the Dolphin* (1967). By 1975 this psychoanalyst and friend of Dr Timothy Leary (the 'turn on, tune in, drop out' 1960s advocate of the benefits of LSD) was calling dolphins 'the humans of the sea' and claiming that they had language skills. By 1978 he had gone right off the rails, speculating that they communicated using telepathy.

Dozens of movies and songs romanticise dolphins. The singers include not just softies like John Denver, but even hardened rockers like the Red Hot Chili Peppers. Their 1987 song, 'Behind The Sun', includes this verse:

My talking dolphin spoke to me.
He spoke to me in symphony.
From freedom's peace beneath the sea,
He looked to me eyes full of love,
Said yes we live behind the sun.

The overall vibe is that dolphins are lovely and caring, with only goodwill and kindness for all other creatures. (I guess we just ignore the fact that they are carnivores that eat other sea creatures.)

Deceptive Dolphins

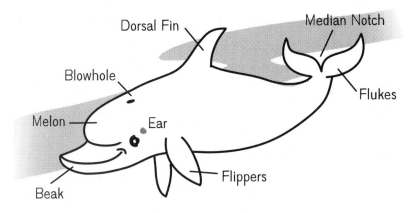

The basic run down of a bottlenose dolphin

The bottlenose dolphin may look like it's always smiling, however it's not a sign of happiness. Their 'smile', or upturned mouth, is in fact a feature of their anatomy.

Dolphin-Assisted Therapy

In fact, some people think that dolphins love us so much that they can heal all human ills.

I first came across this notion when a friend returned from Byron Bay, saying that she was feeling 'extra good', because she had done a lot of 'dolphin work'. In her case, this meant sitting on the beach drinking beer and looking out at the occasional dolphin swimming about in the ocean. The theory goes that dolphins are superior beings who can heal us with their mere presence or with their sonar or spiritual forces such as 'healing energy'.

Indeed, some charlatans have ramped up this simplistic notion into a new and highly lucrative Field of Quackery, giving it the name of DAT, i.e. Dolphin-Assisted Therapy. According to one paper, the proponents claim that DAT can cure a whole gamut of physical and psychological problems, including, but not limited to, 'clinical depression, developmental apraxia, language development, speech development, attention disorders including ADHD, hearing impairments, Down's syndrome, autism, cerebral palsy, chronic pain, cancer, stress, muscular dystrophy, spinal chord (sic) injuries, AIDS, brain injuries, post-traumatic stress disorder, anorexia, trauma from sexual abuse, blindness, and disorders of the immune system'. All of these cures are available, they claim, by swimming or interacting with dolphins, which they can provide — for a fee.

And their fee can be up to $11,800 of your hard-earned cash (air fares and accommodation extra).

Now there's no doubt that hanging around in the open, in lovely weather, with friendly wildlife will make you feel better. But is this the same as a permanent cure? According to several studies that have looked at DAT since it came into existence in the 1970s, the answer is *no*. In fact, just snorkelling around in the open water near a lovely reef, without the dolphins, made people feel just as 'good' as if they had seen dolphins.

Smart Dolphins

Dolphins are quite smart. Studies in 1995 and 2001 claimed that they had awareness of images of themselves in mirrors or video, but this was not corroborated in follow-up studies. However, one study in 2005 did definitely show that they can use sponges as a tool to protect the snout from sharp coral while foraging.

They are certainly intelligent enough to learn tricks when they live in an aquarium. And it does make sense for them to have some kind of communication with each other in the ocean — so that they can round up fish and warn each other about predators, etc.

Science = Real

However, the hard science tells a different story about the supposed eternally calm nature, benevolence and goodwill of dolphins.

Trevor R. Spradlin and his colleagues presented a paper on this topic at the Wild Dolphin Swim Program Workshop. They pointed out that 'people have been seriously injured while trying to interact with wild dolphins' and 'dolphins have been known to bite, ram and pull people under the water's surface'. They also quoted a paper rather scarily entitled, 'Women and children abducted by a wild but sociable adult male bottlenose dolphin'.

Other researchers such as Dr Amy Samuels and her American colleagues have written many articles on dolphins in peer-reviewed journals. They also wrote a chapter for the CSIRO book, *Marine Mammals: Fisheries, Tourism and Management Issues* (2003), edited by Nick Gales and his colleagues.

Dr Samuels looked at four separate 'types' of dolphins.

1 — Solitary Dolphins

One study of 29 solitary dolphins that would seek out human company was particularly illuminating. In this study, only one dolphin, coincidentally called 'Flipper', was praised for 'saving' a drowning boy.

But the remaining 28 dolphins included kidnappers, some who were sexually aggressive, and some with very serious 'anger issues'.

'Donald' and 'Percy' were dolphins who 'achieved notoriety for abducting people who then had to be saved by boat'! About two-thirds (18) were aggressive towards people, causing (among other injuries) a ruptured spleen, fractured ribs and unconsciousness. Nearly half (13) of the dolphins in this study had 'misdirected sexual behaviour towards humans, buoys and/or vessels' — in other words, just about anything that happened to be floating in the water. The authors of *The Book of Animal Ignorance* describe 'misdirected sexual behaviour' very nicely. '... Given that an average male bottlenose weighs 40 stone [about 250 kg or one-quarter of a tonne] and has a foot-long [30 cm], solid muscle penis that ends in a prehensile hook agile enough to catch an eel, you wouldn't want to give off the wrong signals.' Scary, huh!

Mind you, the dolphins' aggressive responses might have been quite justified. 'Percy' suffered a hook in one eye. He ended up disappearing after being exposed to some sewage. 'Donald' had received quite serious wounds from a boat propeller and had also been shot. 'JoJo' had received some 37 injuries from human beings, of which eight were life-threatening.

Dolphins Rescue People, Don't They?

The big story that gets all the pistons going in the same direction is the one about how dolphins love to rescue us from the evil sharks. These stories go back to Greek and Roman times.

Sharks and dolphins eat the same food — and will sometimes pursue each other as they chase the food. If sharks pursue one of the dolphins of a pod, the other dolphins band together to protect the targeted animal, aggressively attacking the shark to drive it away. Marine scientists have often seen this happen. If people happen to be in the water at the same time, they might think that the dolphins are banding together to protect them, not the lone dolphin.

And of course, there are the random events of dolphins going out of their way to rescue people — but it doesn't seem to be their general policy.

2 — Conditioned to People, With Food

The study also looked at dolphins in circumstances where they had been conditioned to feeling at ease with people, by being given food. A typical case involved Monkey Mia, a tourist spot in Western Australia. Here wild dolphins swim to within a metre or so of tourists standing in knee-deep water. The dolphins are encouraged to approach the tourists by being offered food. Indeed, on one of our Outback Trips in 1990, we were some of those tourists.

Dr Samuels' summary is grim — this is harmful to the dolphins.

First, Dr Samuels found that the food that they were given was not as nourishing as fish that they caught for themselves — and was sometimes diseased or partly rotten.

Second, the dolphins were exposed to other risks. The original Monkey Mia dolphin, 'Old Charlie', was shot dead. Another seven of the dolphins died as a result of pollution. In general, the dolphins in these groups showed poor maternal-caring behaviour, which led to reduced survival of their newborn calves. They had also become significantly more aggressive.

The dolphin–human encounter can also be harmful to the visitors. Tourists at Monkey Mia have been bitten by dolphins.

3 — Conditioned to People, No Food

Dr Samuels also looked at dolphins that had been conditioned not to fear people, without giving them food.

It turns out that there has been very little research done on dolphins in this situation. But it is known that they usually change their behaviour when a boat approaches.

4 — Not Conditioned to People

These dolphins have only infrequent contact with people.

With this group, there is a low risk of aggression from the dolphin. However, in one case, a woman nearly died while swimming with a pilot whale (which, despite its name, is actually a member of the dolphin family).

Love or Hate?

Dolphins are not full of love for each other, either. They can be very aggressive towards each other, especially during the mating season.

One study looked at Indian Ocean bottlenose dolphins in Shark Bay in Western Australia. Bottlenose dolphins show their aggression towards each other by their movements, postures and sounds — and they can intensify the aggressive behaviour by slamming their body against another dolphin, or ramming or even biting them.

More than 83% of the dolphins in Shark Bay over the years of this study had tooth-rake marks on their bodies. Male dolphins were often aggressive towards each other. There was also male-against-female aggression, especially when the females were in breeding condition.

Scientists looked at photographs of the dolphins over the years, and counted the tooth-rake marks on their flesh. They also directly observed the dolphins, and saw females being aggressive towards other females every 500 hours. But when there were males involved, this increased to one aggressive act every 61 hours. In about 85% of cases, it was an aggressive male attacking a female.

Rose-Tinted Glasses

The popular media portrays dolphins as cute, happy, playful and friendly. However, this widespread and inaccurate portrayal makes it difficult for the average person to see dolphins as they really are — wild animals. We need to stop seeing them through rose-tinted glasses.

Dolphin or Whale?

There are two major families of dolphins, ranging in size from 1.2 m and 40 kg right up to 9.5 m and 10 tonnes. The most common species is the bottlenose dolphin. There are about five species of river dolphins and about 32 species of ocean dolphins — including about six species commonly, but wrongly, called whales. These 'whales' include the pilot whale and the Killer Whale.

That's right! The Orca, the so-called Killer Whale, is actually a member of the dolphin family. Many of us have seen the impressive footage of an Orca coming up onto a beach to savage a seal. Orcas are not exactly cute and friendly.

Dolphins must have a great PR agency on their team. After all, if they can disown Orca the Dolphin, and turn him into Orca the Killer Whale — well, the agency deserves at least as much applause as a performing dolphin can generate.

The Bottom Drawer Effect

In the Land of Science, the Bottom Drawer Effect relates to what you do with experiments that didn't work, or results that didn't prove anything. You can't bear to throw them away, because they took so much time and effort. So you just shove them into the bottom drawer of your filing cabinet, and leave them there — and nobody else ever knows about them.

A variation on this Bottom Drawer Effect involves results that don't even get recorded, e.g. when the dolphins kill people. They might ram them, bite them to death or just herd them out to sea until they drown. These people will never be able to report the dolphin's aggression towards them — because the dolphins killed them.

The only people who can report back are the ones who lived — and they will tell you how wonderful dolphins are, because they saved their lives.

References

Fraser, John, et al., 'Dolphins in popular literature and media', *Society & Animals*, September 2006, Vol 14, No 4, pp 321–349.

Lloyd, John and Mitchinson, John, *QI: The Book of Animal Ignorance*, London: Faber and Faber, 2007, pp 102, 103.

Mann, J. and Barnett, H., 'Lethal tiger shark (*Galeocerdo cuvier*) attack on bottlenose dolphin (*Tursiops sp.*) calf: Defense and reactions by the mother', *Marine Mammal Science*, April 1999, pp 568–575.

Marino, Lori, et al., 'Dolphin-assisted therapy: More flawed data and more flawed conclusions', *Anthrozoos: A Multidisciplinary Journal of the Interactions of People & Animals*, September 2007, Vol 20, No 3, pp 239–249.

Samuels, Amy, et al., 'A Review of the Literature Pertaining to Swimming with Wild Dolphins', prepared for the Marine Mammal Commission, Maryland, USA, April 2000.

Samuels, Amy, et al., 'Swimming with wild cetaceans, with a special focus on the Southern Hemisphere', Chapter 14 in *Marine Mammals: Fisheries, Tourism and Management Issues*, edited by Nick Gales, et al., Collingwood, Victoria: CSIRO Publishing, 2003.

Scott, Erin M., 'Aggression in bottlenose dolphins: Evidence for sexual coercion, male-male competition, and female tolerance through analysis of tooth-rake marks and behaviour', *Behaviour*, 2005, Vol 142, Issue 1, pp 21–44.

Spradlin, Trevor R., et al., 'Interactions between the public and wild dolphins in the United States: Biological concerns and the *Marine Mammal Protection Act*', Presented at the 'Wild Dolphin Swim Program Workshop' held in conjunction with the 13th Biennial Conference on the Biology of Marine Mammals, 28 November 1999.

Webb, N.G., 'Women and children abducted by a wild but sociable adult male bottlenose dolphin', *Carnivore*, 1978, Vol 1, No 2, pp 89–94.

Dig Those Shooting Stars

One morning when I was about eight years of age, my father took me out to a coconut palm in our front yard. After showing me a hole in the ground (about the size of a golf ball), we started digging down into the hole. The hole continued through one of the roots of the tree and then stopped at a small, round rock. Then he told me that the previous night he had been staring out of the window, waiting for inspiration for another story (he was a writer) when he saw a shooting star zip past — and the golf ball–sized rock that I held in my hand was that shooting star.

At that moment, a myth crumbled, as I realised that a shooting star was not really a star falling out of the sky.

Meteoroid, Meteor, Meteorite?

'Stars' are huge objects, typically a million or more kilometres in diameter, burning with nuclear fires — and very far away from the Earth. Many of them have planets orbiting around them.

On the other hand, so-called 'shooting stars' are quite different — they are small rocks burning up in our atmosphere.

The naming of these rocks is a bit confusing. The word 'meteor'

How to make a crater in 4 easy steps

A meteor about to become a meteorite

A meteorite impacts

a) The impact

b) It's a gas

The projectile vapourises and a shockwave spreads through the surface of the planet.

c) Hitting hard

Ejecta are thrown out of the crater.

d) Let cool and it's done

Most of the ejected bits falls back to the surface to form secondary craters.

comes from the Greek word *meteora*, which means 'things in the air', or 'high up in the atmosphere'. This ancient Greek word has given us the English words 'meteorology', the study of the weather, and 'meteoritics', the study of meteorites.

When these rocks are zipping through Space, they are called 'meteoroids'. They range in size from millionths of a metre to metres in diameter. Once the meteoroids enter the atmosphere, leaving a visible, bright streak in the air, they are called 'meteors'.

And after they have landed, the lump of rock that you see on the ground is called a 'meteorite'.

Meteoroid to Meteor ...

Let's look at a meteoroid zipping through Space.

Speed has to be measured relative to some object, so let's measure it relative to the Earth. Typically, the object can be moving through the solar system at speeds of between zero and 60 km/sec (216,000 kph). As it gets closer to the Earth, it gradually speeds up thanks to the Earth's gravitational field, picking up another 11 km/sec of speed. So the meteoroid will hit the upper reaches of our atmosphere with a minimum speed of 11 km/sec (39,600 kph) and possibly a maximum speed of approximately 71 km/sec.

The Kinetic Energy increases enormously as the speed of the object increases. So even the relatively 'slow' speed of 11 km/sec gives the meteoroid ten times as much energy as the same weight of a high explosive such as TNT. Once it hits the thin atmosphere about 100 km above the ground, this energy appears in a few forms.

Most of the energy appears as heat. It vaporises the surface of the meteor, turning it into a liquid and then a gas. (The rock is in the Earth's atmosphere, so it's now called a 'meteor'.)

The molten surface of the meteor is whisked away behind the meteor by its speed, and appears as a tail of ionised atoms. About 0.1–1% of the energy of the incoming meteor is turned into visible light, which we see as the tail of the meteor. Strictly speaking, the name 'meteor' refers to both the moving rock *and* the tail behind it.

Some of the energy of the meteor turns into a shock wave. This can sometimes be heard as a sonic boom. The shock wave can be so strong that it can register on seismometers down on the ground.

The shock wave also acts upon the meteor itself. The structural integrity of the meteor can vary enormously — from as weak as a clod of dirt, to as strong as a ball of iron. In some cases, the shock wave can break up, or fragment, the meteor.

As it falls deeper into the thicker atmosphere, the rock slows down and gets cooler. So the tail usually peters out at about 80 km above the ground, but it sometimes survives to an altitude of 50 km. The so-called visible flight takes only a few seconds.

So while a meteor is real, most of it is as intangible as a rainbow.

Atom Bombs from Space

About seven to eight times each year, US military satellites see a big lump of rock explode in the upper atmosphere with the energy of a small atom bomb. These lumps are too big to vaporise harmlessly in the atmosphere, but are too small to punch through the atmosphere and make it all the way to the ground. So, on average, they explode about 30 km above the ground.

We only found out about this in the mid-1990s, after the data had been first declassified by the US Defense Department. The military satellites saw some 136 atom-bomb-size explosions between 1975 and 1992. According to scientists, the satellites probably see only 10% of all these explosions.

In 1994, President Bill Clinton was woken in the middle of the night because one such explosion was thought to be a human-made atomic explosion.

Brightest Meteor Ever

It seems that the brightest meteor ever recorded was the one that impacted the Tunguska region of central Siberia around 7.14 am, on 30 June 1908. The rock, probably about 40–50 m in diameter, created an airburst explosion at an altitude of about 5–10 km above the ground.

According to eyewitness accounts, it was as bright as the Sun. The incoming meteor was so big and moving so fast, that it flattened an estimated 80 million trees over about 2,000 km^2 of countryside. It delivered the energy equivalent to a 10-megaton nuclear weapon.

Meteor to Meteorite

Most of the rocks do not make it down to the ground — they simply vaporise entirely or break up into smaller fragments that then vaporise.

The ones that do survive need a fairly low entry speed (say under 25 km/sec), so there is less energy available to destroy them. They also need to start off with a fairly large mass (say, at least 100–1,000 g) and be strong enough to resist the crushing effect of the shock wave.

These rocks will usually have lost all of their supersonic velocity at an altitude of between 5 and 25 km. They will then fall at a 'terminal velocity' of between 150 and 300 kph. This terminal velocity is a result of the balance between two forces — the 'suck' of gravity and the resistance of the wind.

The 'dark flight' of the meteor down to the ground can take a few minutes.

If the landing is noticed, it is usually only as a whistle and a dull thud. However, there have been a few rare cases where a meteor(ite) has smashed into the back end of a stationary car, landed just in front of the head of a sunbather on a beach, or even come through a roof and grazed the abdomen of an inhabitant of a house.

Where Do Meteors Come From?

We are not exactly sure where meteors come from.

Certainly, quite a lot of them come from the so-called Asteroid Belt between Mars and Jupiter. It is almost entirely empty Space — nothing at all like you see in the movies, where the spacecraft has to swerve frantically to avoid hitting an asteroid or being hit by one. But given enough time, asteroids do occasionally collide, creating rubble. Sometimes this rubble eventually makes it to Earth. We have discovered this by matching the colour of meteorites with the colour of various asteroids.

Some meteors are associated with comets. On one hand, we now think of comets as dirty iceballs of rubble and dust. But let's think of a comet as a truck with a dirty exhaust, looping around the Sun in an elliptical orbit that might take up to several hundred years to complete. The comet is continually shedding material — huge amounts when it is close to the heat of the Sun and hardly any when it is in the depths of cold Space. Eventually, after many many orbits of the Sun, the entire path that the comet takes on its elliptical orbit is filled with rubble and ice from the comet. Typically, the Earth will cross this orbit at around the same time each year, and there will be a meteor shower. There are a dozen or so known meteor showers. Leonid meteor showers occur annually in mid-November, but every 33–34 years, they really light up the sky. The Leonids are associated with the Comet Tempel-Tuttle.

Surprisingly, a very tiny number of meteorites appear to come from the Moon or Mars. It seems that meteors have, in the distant past, smashed into the surface of the Moon or Mars with such force that they have splashed bits of rock from the Moon and Mars into Space. After thousands or millions of years of floating in Space, these rocks were captured by the Earth's gravitational field, making it down to the ground for us to find.

Close Encounters

The most recent rock that came closest to actually hitting the Earth probably zipped past on 31 March 2004. On that day, the meteoroid known as 2004 FU162 missed the Earth by about the radius of the Earth — about 6,500 km. Measuring only about 10 m in diameter, it would almost certainly have exploded in the upper atmosphere — and caused no damage.

However, on 19 May 1996, the rock JA1 missed us by about 450,000 km — roughly the distance from the Earth to the Moon. As it was a lot bigger — about 500 m in diameter — it would have caused a lot of damage if it had hit the Earth.

In most cases, we find out about these objects only after they have missed hitting Earth, when astronomers are examining old photographs. Even though these rocks could end civilisation as we know it if they hit our planet, less money is actually spent looking for them than is spent making movies about them — e.g. movies like *Armageddon* and *Deep Impact*.

What Are Meteors Made Of?

Most of the meteorites, about 82%, are predominantly stony. Inside these meteorites are small spheres of silicate called 'chondrules'. So the stony meteorites that are made of these chondrules are called 'chondrites'. Another 8% of meteorites are stony, but do not contain chondrules. These are called 'stony achondrites'.

About 5% of meteorites are predominantly iron. Predictably, they are called 'iron' meteorites.

Of course, those that have a mix of iron and chondrules are called 'stony iron' meteorites.

Surprisingly, about 90% of meteorites have enough iron to be attracted by a magnet.

Meteor Shower/Storm

On a dark, moonless and cloudless night, according to the experts you should probably be able to see about five to ten meteors per hour. Every time that my family and I have been in the Outback, we usually see about 25 per hour. However, this is with a team of three or four of us checking out the entire sky.

But you can get rates much higher than this. Back in November 1966, the Leonid Meteor Storm showered North America with shooting stars at rates of up to 100 per second.

God's TV

My family and I have spent a total of about two years travelling through the Australian Outback. Our evening routine is always the same.

We have an early dinner and then cuddle up on a big ground sheet in our swags. And then, armed only with our eyes and a laser, we spend the first hour and a half after sunset looking for satellites. Typically, we will see about 25. We use the laser to point out the very faint ones. We then spend the next hour and a half looking for falling stars — and again, we usually see about 25.

But in all this time, we have never been lucky enough to have one land near us. (And we have never been unlucky enough to have one thump into us.)

I still have the falling star that my father and I dug up — and yes, it is an iron-type meteorite, and no, it is not a star.

Cosmic Dust per Year

Meteors and other cosmic dust have been falling into our atmosphere ever since our planet sprung into existence.

A recent study looked at various isotopes of helium in Antarctic ice. It revealed that the Earth is getting heavier by about 40,000 tonnes each year — and that this weight gain has been relatively constant for the past 30,000 years.

References

Comins, Neil F., *Heavenly Errors: Misconceptions About the Real Nature of the Universe*, New York: Columbia University Press, 2001, pp 46, 64.

Fernandez, Liubomir and McDonnell, Patrick J., 'Meteorite causes a stir in Peru: The explosion near Carancas frightened and awed residents and (they say) made them sick', Special to The Times, 21 September 2007, *Los Angeles Times*.

Winckler, Gisela and Fischer, Hubertus, '30,000 years of cosmic dust in Antarctic ice', *Science*, 28 July 2006, Vol 313, No 5786, p 491.

Ring-a-Ring o'Roses

We have all heard the children's nursery rhyme that runs something like:

Ring-a-ring o'roses,
A pocket full of posies,
A-tishoo! A-tishoo!
We all fall down.

The rhyme is usually accompanied by a little dance. The children all hold hands, form a circle, and then run or skip until they fall into the middle in a heap on top of each other.

The standard explanation about the origin of this game is that this charming little nursery rhyme describes the symptoms and rapid demise of anyone suffering from that terrible medieval disease — the Black Death. Although it may well be a catchy tune, it has nothing to do with the plague.

Black Death 101

In 1347 the Bubonic Plague, commonly known as the Black Death, swept across Europe. It was caused by a bacterium living on fleas carried by rats, and it re-emerged every spring, spreading further each year. In five years, the Bubonic Plague had killed one in every three people in Europe. By 1352 the population of Europe had plummeted from 75 million to 50 million. This disaster led to labour shortages, political turmoil, and religious and philosophical questionings. (Fortunately, the regular visitations of the plague slowed down over the next few centuries.)

The disease was devastating, killing its victims within several days, sometimes sooner. It came in a few different versions, depending on how it was transmitted, and the robustness of the victim.

A-tishoo! A-tishoo! We all fall down
(apparently from Bubonic Plague)

Rosy rashes and sneezing weren't really symptoms of the plague ... but falling down (dead) kinda was pretty accurate.

The Bubonic Plague was the most common form of the disease (about 90% of all cases). The victims suffered from large swellings of the lymph nodes in the groin, neck and armpits. These swellings then burst through the skin, oozing pus and blood. At this stage they were known as 'buboes', hence the name Bubonic Plague. The fingers would turn black from gangrene, as would the various areas on the body that bled — giving the disease its other name, the Black Death. The victims also suffered from headaches, painful joints, nausea and vomiting. About 80% of the victims died within eight days. Today, modern treatments can reduce the death rate to less than 5%.

Eyewitness Account – 1

Marchione di Coppo Stefani, who was born in Florence, was 12 years of age when the Bubonic Plague struck. He wrote about these dreadful events in the late 1370s and early 1380s.

He described how frightful the disease was, and how it killed not just people but all of their animals, both house pets and farm animals. As the epidemic worsened, the survivors could not bury the dead properly. Because there was neither the time nor the inclination to dig individual graves, deep trenches were dug at every church. People would sneak in at night and just toss the bodies into the trench for free, or do it by daylight and pay for the privilege. 'The next morning, if there were many [bodies] in the trench, they covered them over with dirt. And then more bodies were put on top of them, with a little more dirt over those; they put layer on layer just like one puts layers of cheese in a lasagna.'

The Pneumonic Plague (about 9% of cases) resulted from the bacterium being transmitted, not by the fleas, but directly from the lungs of one infected person to another. In this case, the victims coughed up blood. The disease had a 90–95% death rate.

The least common (1%), but most virulent and fast-acting, form was the Septicaemic Plague, the bacterium transmitted directly into the blood. The death rate was 100%.

Such was the rapid decline in the health of an infected person, that the Italian author Giovanni Boccaccio wrote that the victims 'ate lunch with their friends and dinner with their ancestors in paradise'. He was probably referring to the Septicaemic Plague.

Not a Bacterium?

The conventional belief is that the Black Death was caused by a bacterium carried by fleas on rats. The French bacteriologist Alexandre Yersin helped to isolate this bacterium, hence its scientific name *Yersinia pestis*.

But there have always been conflicting theories. One of the latest has been suggested by Susan Scott and Christopher Duncan, epidemiologists from the University of Liverpool. For various reasons, they claim that the Black Death is caused by a virus similar to the Ebola virus.

Time will tell ...

It Wasn't Around Then ...

So it all sounds very reasonable that this terrible series of rolling plagues would make its way into the popular culture. And what is more popular than a nursery rhyme sung by little kiddies?

And this is where we hit the first problem with the myth.

Unfortunately, the nursery rhyme was totally unknown for over 400 years after the plague hit Europe. During this long period of time — over four centuries — there were many eager hunters of nursery rhymes keen to document any rhyme they could find. However, there was not one single written reference to this rhyme before 1881, according to the authoritative *Oxford Dictionary of Nursery Rhymes*, edited by Iona and Peter Opie.

In fact, if this verse really did date back to 1347 and the Bubonic Plague, it would be older than Chaucer's *Canterbury Tales*. So why aren't there any versions of this rhyme in Middle English?

There is a similar nursery rhyme that was later described as being sung in New Bedford, Massachusetts around 1790. But the very first appearance in print of the 'Ring-a-Ring-a-Roses' nursery rhyme is in Kate Greenaway's *Mother Goose or The Old Nursery Rhymes* in 1881.

There Are Too Many Versions ...

The second problem is that there are many dozens of versions of this nursery rhyme, and only a very few could be interpreted as referring to the Bubonic Plague.

In fact, the first known version from Massachusetts does not seem to be related at all to the Bubonic Plague.

Ring-a-ring-a-rosie,
A bottle full of posie,
All the girls in our town
Ring for little Josie.

And here's another version from the UK, which again seems to have nothing to do with the Bubonic Plague.

The King has sent his daughter,
To fetch a pail of water.
Ash-a! Ash-a!
We all kneel down.

And just to hammer this home, here's yet another version which would require a lot of imagination to link it to the Bubonic Plague.

The Wedding Bells are ringing,
And boys and girls are singing,
Ash-a! Ash-a!
All fall down.

It's Wrong ...

And here's the third problem. The nursery rhyme is not very accurate at depicting the symptoms of someone suffering from the Bubonic Plague.

No, a 'rosy' rash was not one of the symptoms of the Bubonic Plague. There were many manifestations in the skin, but a rosy rash was not one of them.

'A pocket full of posies'? Over the years, there have been many interpretations of this line. They include the claim that this line really referred to the pus hidden under the skin before it oozed out; or something that you would put in the grave with the deceased; or flowers on the grave; or yes, something to either ward off the plague or to mask the stench of the rotting corpses.

'A-tishoo'? Well, sneezing was not one of the symptoms of the disease. So some people have said that it should be 'ashes', which is what we turn into when we are cremated. However, in the panic of the Black Death, very few people were cremated — most of the dead were simply left where they fell and, much later, thrown into trenches.

'We all fall down'? Well yes, when you die you might fall down (although not if you die in bed). But in many versions of this nursery rhyme, the players do not fall down at the end, but curtsey to each other. A curtsey is a gracious bending movement, not linked to morbid deaths in any way.

Eyewitness Account – 2

The Italian poet and author Giovanni Boccaccio (1313–1375) wrote *The Decameron*. He also lived through the Black Death. He wrote: '… it began with swellings in the groin and armpit … some … as big as apples … some … shaped like eggs … appear over the entire body … covered with dark and livid spots … some were large and widely spaced while some were small and bunched together.'

So How?

So how did the myth of this nursery rhyme describing the Black Death arise?

We can look to James Leasor, who in 1961 wrote *The Plague and the Fire*. As far as we can tell, he was the first to link the verse to the Black Death — six centuries after the plague first swept through Europe.

Blame Mr Leasor.

But how did the myth then take off? Two reasons. First, with so many versions of 'Ring-a-Ring o'Roses', all the versions that don't fit were simply ignored. Second, virtually any meaning can be read into *any* song or verse — if you try hard enough.

And remember, if all attempts to twist the meaning of the songs to your purpose fail, well, you can always try playing them backwards. With a lot of effort, you might even manage to find references to Satan Himself …

References

MacKenzie, Debora, 'Ring a ring o'roses, A pocket full of posies, Atishoo! Atishoo! We all fall down', *New Scientist*, 24 November 2001, p 34.

Opie, Iona and Peter (Editors), *The Oxford Dictionary of Nursery Rhymes*, Oxford, UK: Oxford University Press, 1989, pp 364, 365.

Black Death

The Black Death was a horribly devastating pandemic of the Middle Ages. In the mid-1300s, the Black Death killed one-third of the population of Europe — a truly overwhelming and shocking catastrophe. Today, most Westerners believe that the Black Death of the 1300s began in Europe. This is not true.

History of Epidemics and Pandemics

More than a dozen major epidemics and pandemics have been documented in human history.

Probably the earliest known epidemic — reported in *I Samuel* 5:6 in the Torah — dates back to the 11th century BC. In 430 BC, the Plague of Athens killed one-third of the city's inhabitants.

The first known pandemic was possibly the Plague of Justinian. It started in the region of Egypt or Ethiopia (in 541 AD), subsequently spreading to the then major city of Constantinople. At its peak, it killed 10,000 people per day. The Plague of Justinian eventually wiped out one-quarter of the inhabitants of the Eastern Mediterranean Region. In total, this pandemic killed about 100 million people in its first century of activity.

Some 800 years later (in the mid-1300s), the pandemic known as the Black Death made its appearance. At the time, it was called 'The Great Mortality', but later historians called it the 'Black Death'. The word 'black' here is derived from either the blackened skin of the victims, or from another meaning of 'black', i.e. 'gloomy', 'terrible' or 'without hope'.

But pandemics have also occurred in more recent times.

Between 1855 and 1959, the Third Pandemic emerged from China and then swept across the world, killing 12 million people. (The Plague of Justinian was the first pandemic, the Black Death the second — this was the third.) In 1894, it killed approximately 90,000 people in Hong Kong and Canton. But by 1959, the worldwide death rate had dropped to 200 per year.

And after World War I, the Great Influenza (also known as Spanish Flu) Pandemic erupted out of Fort Riley, Kansas, in 1918. This was the Fourth Pandemic. Technological advances in means of transport had sped up travel between countries, making it easier to spread the disease quickly across the globe. By 1920 it had killed 50–100 million people worldwide.

Pandemic or Epidemic?

A pandemic is like an epidemic, but bigger — it's the Military-Industrial Full-Blown Version.

In Greek, *epi* means 'upon' and *demos* means 'people', so an epidemic is an affliction upon the people. However, *pan* means 'all', so a pandemic affects all the people.

Black Death of the 1300s

The Black Death almost certainly arose in 1334 in the Chinese province of Hubei. About 90% of the people in Hubei died in the initial outbreak. (Some two-thirds of the populations in eight other areas of China died in revisitations of this Black Death from 1353 to 1354.)

The Black Death appears to have spread to Europe along the Mongol trading routes. Its first major Eastern European contact was in Caffa, a trading city on the Crimean peninsula. (Caffa, currently called Feodossija or Feodosiya, is in the Ukraine. If Europeans remain true to their millennia-old tradition and continue to invade each other's countries, and change the borders, who knows what this city will be called in the future.)

Caffa is famous as the site of one of the earliest instances of using biological warfare as a weapon of war. You have probably heard the story of disease-ridden corpses being hurled into a besieged city — Caffa was almost certainly that city.

Biological Warfare

In World War II, the Japanese actually used the Black Death bacterium *Yersinia pestis* as a weapon. The infamous Unit 731, in then occupied Manchuria, deliberately infected both prisoners of war and Chinese civilians with the bacterium. To dehumanise the victims, they were called 'logs' by the Japanese.

In the Cold War, the Soviets built up huge stockpiles of the bacterium for use in the event of an all-out war.

Caffa — Trading City

The coastal city of Caffa on the Black Sea was ideally situated. By land, caravan routes connected it to the Far East. By water, it allowed easy trade to central Russia and Moscow via the mighty 2,000 km long Don River. For this reason, the great Genoese merchant ships used Caffa as their main trading port on the Black Sea in the 1200s and 1300s.

Caffa was originally founded in the 6th century BC by the Greeks from Miletos, who called it Theodosia. The Greeks probably chose this location because of the rich surrounding agricultural lands, which provided produce for trade. The city traded successfully as a port for a millennium, until the Huns destroyed it in the 4th century AD.

It remained a minor village for about another millennium. In 1266, the Khan of the Golden Horde (the Mongols) re-established it as a trading port in an agreement with the Genoese. But relations between the Mongols and the Genoese were always uneasy and, over the years, it was besieged, set fire to and abandoned, before being finally re-established in 1312.

In the 1340s the thriving Genoese city of Caffa was very cosmopolitan, accommodating not just the Genoese, but also Turks, Venetians, Armenians, Greeks, Jews and yes, Mongols. It was very heavily fortified by two strong concentric walls, with 6,000 homes inside the inner wall, and 11,000 inside the outer wall.

For various reasons, relations between the Genoese and the Mongols again deteriorated. The Mongol leader Janiberg besieged Caffa in 1343, was pushed back by an Italian relief force in 1344, but renewed the siege in 1345. In 1346, after a long trip from China, the Black Death reached the besieging Mongol troops.

Black Death

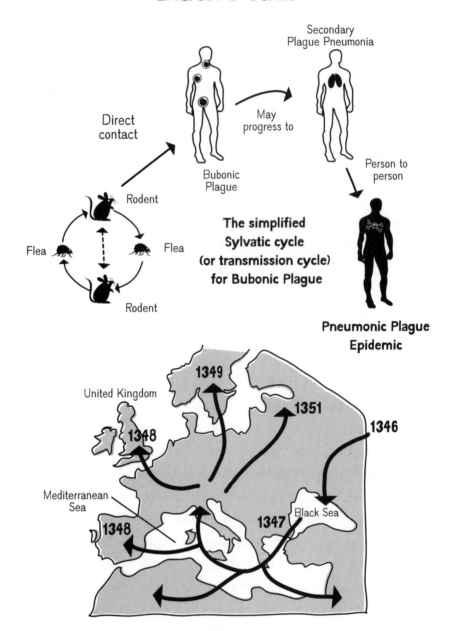

Secondary
Plague Pneumonia

Direct
contact

May
progress to

Bubonic
Plague

Person to
person

Rodent

Flea

Flea

The simplified
Sylvatic cycle
(or transmission cycle)
for Bubonic Plague

Rodent

Pneumonic Plague
Epidemic

1349

United Kingdom

1351

1346

1348

Mediterranean
Sea

1348

1347

Black Sea

How the Black Death 'got around' in the early days

Flying Corpses

We do not have eyewitness accounts of the effects of the Black Death on the actual siege. But we do have the accounts of Gabriele de' Mussi, who lived from c. 1280 to c. 1356. He definitely does not claim to have seen what he describes at the siege of Caffa, because he writes: 'Now it is time that we passed from east to west to discuss all the things which we ourselves have seen …' So he implies that his reports from Caffa (in the East) are second-hand, while his descriptions from Genoa (in the West) are based on his personal observations. However, he seems to be reliable, because his accounts of other events are consistent and, in agreement with, other writers.

The Black Death struck the Mongols who were attacking the city of Caffa, killing 'thousands upon thousands every day'. They died almost as soon as the swellings appeared in their armpits and groins. Gabriele de' Mussi writes: 'The dying Tartars, stunned and stupefied by the immensity of the disaster brought about by the disease, and realising that they had no hope of escape, lost interest in the siege. But they ordered corpses to be placed in catapults and lobbed into the city in the hope that the intolerable stench would kill everyone inside.'

It sounds very reasonable.

Historical records tell us that a military trebuchet (a large medieval siege engine for hurling missiles) could hurl a 100 kg load some 300 m — modern reconstructions of trebuchets have easily reached 200 m. The diseased corpses would have been badly mangled by the impact of landing, and bodily fluids would have gone splattering in all directions. The defenders themselves would have had cuts and abrasions thanks to the siege, and could have, therefore, become easily infected. Direct transmission of the plague from person to person is still common. Between 1970 and 1995 there were about 284 cases of plague recorded in the USA. In about 20% of the cases, the bacterium was transmitted directly from one person to another.

Trebuchet or Catapult?

Both a catapult and a trebuchet are military devices that hurl stuff at the enemy, but they work by different methods.

A catapult relies on some sort of stored energy — usually the tension in stretched or twisted ropes. Typically, a catapult is limited to loads of 30–40 kg.

A trebuchet relies on counterweights. It can easily hurl loads weighing 100 kg or more.

Further Spread

The Genoese inhabitants of Caffa fled back to their homes in southern Europe, taking the disease with them. Their arrival home was both bizarre and disastrous. The ships limped into ports or were washed up on the shores, most or all of the crew dead. Rescuers and visitors to the ships became infected.

Even without Caffa, the Black Death would have invaded Europe. The stream of infection from Caffa was just one of the many routes that the Black Death took into Europe.

It spread west via the other trading ports in the Black Sea, arriving in Constantinople in 1347.

Overland caravans also carried the disease into Europe. Several Italian merchant ships carried the disease to Sicily when they docked in October 1347. An eyewitness wrote: '… soon death was everywhere. Fathers abandoned their sick sons. Lawyers refused to come and make out wills for the dying. Friars and nuns were left to care for the sick, and monasteries and convents were soon deserted, as they were stricken too. Bodies were left in empty houses, and there was no one to give them a Christian burial.'

By January 1348, the Black Death had spread to Genoa and Venice. By June 1348, it had reached England, France, Spain and Portugal. It took two more years to reach Scandinavia and another year to get to northwestern Russia. The Black Death also devastated the Middle East, reaching Antioch in 1348–1349, Mecca and Mosul (then Mawsil) in 1349 and Yemen in 1351. It then kept returning, with major recurrences in 1361–1363, 1369–1371, 1374–1375, 1390 and 1400.

With each successive return of the plague, fewer people died, because the genetically susceptible people had already perished in earlier outbreaks. Even so, the population of Europe returned to pre-plague levels only in the early 1500s.

After this, there were a number of recurrences — the Italian Plague (1629–1631), the Great Plague of London (1665–1666), the Great Plague of Marseille (1720–1722) and the Plague Riot in Moscow (1771).

Results of Black Death

The Black Death was many things, but it was not unique to Europe, nor (as mentioned earlier) did it start there — it came from China.

In Europe, the successive revisitations of the Black Death caused, of course, massive depopulation. The population of Europe dropped from 75 million to 50 million. In Damascus, some 25–40% of the people died, with 1,000 dying horribly each day at the peak of the outbreak. The population of Florence dropped from 120,000 in 1338 to just 50,000 in 1351. In England, the population dropped from seven million before the arrival of the Black Death, to only two million in 1400.

Unsurprisingly, there were also major and long-reaching social effects of the Black Death.

The peasants who survived found themselves highly sought after as a source of labour. The landowners resented this because, for the first time, the peasants were not easy to replace and no longer a source of very cheap labour. By the end of the 1300s, there had been peasant uprisings in France (the Jacquerie Rebellion), Italy (the Ciompi Rebellion), Belgium and England (the English Peasant Revolt). Social barriers between the poor and the rich were torn asunder. Desperate laws (the Sumptuary Laws) were passed to stop peasants with newly acquired wealth from wearing the trappings of the rich.

It is also claimed that the sudden geographical movements of many English-speaking people led to the Great Vowel Shift, in which the pronunciation of the English language changed dramatically. The German, Icelandic and Dutch languages also experienced changes in pronunciation, similar to those in the English Great Vowel Shift.

The Roman Catholic Church was ineffectual against the plague and lost much of its influence.

It is even claimed that the Renaissance — the rise of classical scholarship and scientific and geographical discoveries in Europe — was a direct result of the Black Death.

They say that every cloud has a silver lining — although in this case, it was a really Big Black Cloud.

Peak of Evolution

We humans might think that because our Big Brains invented music, weapons of mass destruction and income tax, we must be at the top of the evolutionary chain. But bacteria, viruses and parasites don't care about our fabulous achievements — they just want to survive and reproduce.

Today there is still much controversy over which infectious agent (bacteria, virus, etc.) caused which pandemic/epidemic. Certainly, epidemiologists all agree that the Third Pandemic was caused by the bacterium, *Yersinia pestis*. Most of them believe that this bacterium also caused the Black Death of the 1300s. However, there are a few odd details that cause disagreements among some epidemiologists. These include the speed at which the epidemic spreads, the different rates of death, and the effect of local temperatures.

References

Del Re, Gerard, *The Whole Truth: A Compendium of Myths, Mistakes, and Misconceptions*, New York: Random House, 2004, p 35.

Drancourt, M., Houhamdi, L. and Raoult, D., '*Yersinia pestis* as a telluric, human ectoparasite-borne organism', *Lancet Infectious Diseases*, April 2006, Vol 6, Issue 4, pp 234–241.

Encyclopædia Britannica, Ultimate Reference Suite DVD, 2006 — 'Black Death'.

Wheelis, Mark, 'Biological warfare at the 1346 Siege of Caffa', *Emerging Infectious Diseases*, September 2002, pp 971–975.

Fuelish Car Engine Idling

I've had a lot of fun teaching the junior members of my family how to drive the Family Chariot. But along the way, I realised that something I had done for a long time was actually wrong. Previously, I tried to be 'kind' to my car's engine by allowing it to idle for quite a while before I pulled away from the kerb.

But when I began investigating the Science Behind It All, I found that a long idle was actually harming the engine, the environment — and my wallet.

Don't Idle

The powertrain of a car refers to the mechanical components that make the car go. The power starts at the engine, goes through the gearbox and finishes at the driving wheels. Les Ryder, the chief powertrain engineer from Ford, USA, said in the January 2007 issue of *Popular Mechanics*, 'Engines run best at their design temperature'. In other words, Mr Ryder is telling us that engines run most cleanly and efficiently somewhere between 85°C and 95°C. Idling is not the best or quickest way to warm up your engine — gentle driving is.

The Canadian Office of Energy Efficiency agrees that the best way to warm up your engine is to drive it. Even if the outside temperature is –20°C, they recommend that you idle the engine for only 15–30 seconds before pulling out onto the road. And you need even less idling time at the temperatures usually experienced in Australia.

Cold Idling Engines

Idling a cold engine to 'warm it up' is bad in so many ways.

In a cold engine, the fuel is not completely burnt, so it condenses into droplets on the cylinder walls. This leads to two kinds of damage inside the engine.

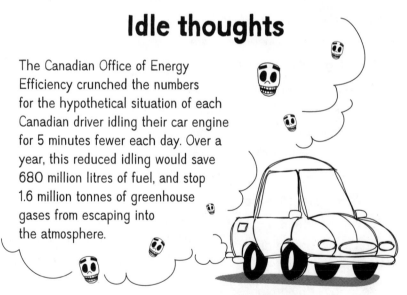

Idle thoughts

The Canadian Office of Energy Efficiency crunched the numbers for the hypothetical situation of each Canadian driver idling their car engine for 5 minutes fewer each day. Over a year, this reduced idling would save 680 million litres of fuel, and stop 1.6 million tonnes of greenhouse gases from escaping into the atmosphere.

A passenger-empty, idling car 'warming up' nothing more than the Earth's atmosphere.

First, the droplets of raw unburnt fuel wash the lubricating oil off the cylinder walls. Without this protective coating of oil the cylinder walls wear very rapidly.

Second, the unburnt fuel flows down the walls and slips past the rings — diluting the oil in the sump. Diluted oil is not as good a lubricant as pure oil.

Idling also drops the temperature of the spark plugs. This can cause dirty plugs, which can worsen your fuel consumption by some 5%.

Glazing the Bore

If a brand-new or reconditioned engine is badly 'run in' by the owner, the engine can burn too much oil for its entire life.

The engine consumes extra oil through a phenomenon called 'glazing'. You need just a tiny amount of 'roughness' to give good contact between the rings and the cylinder walls. The bore is manufactured with a deliberate diamond-like or crosshatching pattern on its walls to create a small, but definite, amount of friction. But when 'glazing' occurs, the rings 'rub' on the walls of the cylinder, making them too smooth, i.e. 'glazed' like glass. The oil blows past the rings and out the exhaust pipe.

I know of two driver behaviours that can glaze the bore. The first is idling the engine for too long while it's new. The second is driving for too long on cruise control with a new engine on flat countryside. In this case, the engine sits on the same engine revs for extended periods of time, thus smoothing out the diamond-like pattern.

New Idling Engines

Excessive idling can also damage new engines.

Inside a new engine, the piston rings need a reasonable load in order to 'settle' into the grooves (known as 'lands') on the walls of the piston. Too much idling means that the rings won't settle in properly. The rings can rattle, cause strange wear patterns on the cylinder wall and may even crack.

Therefore, with a new or reconditioned engine, you should accelerate away within a few seconds of starting — but not with a 'lead foot' — to keep a steady load on the rings. This is easy to do from a cold start, providing you keep the engine revs fairly low for the first 3–5 minutes. This gives the oil a chance to warm up and get thinner, so that it can flow easily into all the small clearances inside the engine.

Exhausted Idling Engines

You might have noticed a vapour trailing out of the exhaust of some cars in the early morning. This is not the oil vapour of a worn engine but the normal water vapour from a cold engine. So the longer you idle the engine, the longer it will take to warm up. And more water droplets will be deposited inside your exhaust system — making it rust sooner.

With a long idle time the engine will produce many more unwanted pollutants. For example, modern cars have catalytic converters. When they reach their normal operating temperature (400–800°C), they convert nasty pollutants into fewer nasty chemicals. And you guessed it, the quickest way for catalytic converters to reach their normal operating temperature is by driving, not idling. The longer you idle your engine, the longer your catalytic converter will remain too cold to do its job.

Problem and Cure

On an average day in the middle of winter, Canadians will idle their car engines for a total of 75 million minutes. This works out to be one car idling for over 142 years! For this reason, Canada has started a national campaign to reduce the unnecessary idling of engines. There are similar regional campaigns in Japan and the UK. In the USA, 13 states have now passed laws regulating the idling of engines. And the ski resort town of Aspen, in Colorado, has actually passed laws making it illegal for car engines to idle for more than five minutes.

Automotive engineers are now talking about the benefits of switching off your engine in traffic, if you are going to be stopped for more than ten seconds.

However, this is contrary to the philosophy behind the Remote Start Function. Available in some US cars, it lets you start the engine from about 60 m away. The advantage is that you can walk out of your house into a nice warm car. The disadvantage is that in ten minutes of idling, you burn about half a litre of fuel.

City of Aspen Municipal Code

13.08.110 Engine Idling.

(a) Except as hereinafter provided, it shall be unlawful for any person to idle or permit the idling of the motor of any stationary motor vehicle for a prolonged or unreasonable period of time determined herein to be five (5) minutes or more within any one (1) hour period of time.

(b) This section shall not apply when an engine must be operated in the idle mode for safety reasons including, but not limited to, the operation of cranes and fork lifts used in the construction industry.

The Canadian Office of Energy Efficiency crunched the numbers for the hypothetical situation of each Canadian driver idling their car engine for five minutes fewer each day. Over a year, this reduced idling would save 680 million litres of fuel and stop 1.6 million tonnes of greenhouse gases from escaping into the atmosphere.

The best way to warm an engine is to drive it gently. When you idle a car, you get zero kilometres per litre, lots of pollution — and a hole in your wallet.

Idling in Traffic

Yes, it does take a little extra fuel to start a cold engine in the morning. But it takes very little extra fuel to start an engine that is already warm. So if you have to stop in traffic for more than 5–10 seconds, switch off the engine.

References

Allen, Mike, 'Warm the engine first? Debunking more of dad's myths', *Popular Mechanics*, March 2007.

Dunne, Jim, 'Your dad was wrong: A lot of traditional automotive wisdom just doesn't hold up', *Popular Mechanics*, January 2007.

'Fuelish Myths', *Time*, Vol 114, No 2, 17 September 1979.

Magliozzi, Tom, Magliozzi, Ray and Berman, Doug, 'Click & clack: Hot air on AC', *Washington Post*, 8 April 2007.

Office of Transportation and Air Quality, US Environmental Protection Agency, 'Compilation of State, County, and Local Anti-Idling Regulations', EPA420-B-06-004, April 2006, p 26.

Cranberry Juice and Urinary Tract Infections

Urinary Tract Infections (UTIs) are very common in women. And cranberry juice does have a place in preventing recurring UTIs, but it can't get rid of an established infection.

UTI — Stats and Micropathology

Most men will never have a UTI. However, about half of all women will have a UTI at some stage in their life.

Unfortunately, about one-third of women who have a UTI will have a recurrence in the following year. The major risk groups are women aged 25–29 years (sexual activity is a risk factor) and over 55 years (caused by lower levels of protective oestrogen).

In the USA, approximately 7–11 million women are prescribed antibacterials for their UTIs. Each year UTIs cost the American community US$1.6 billion in direct and indirect costs. Each year UTIs in female university students result in 6.1 days of suffering the symptoms before the treatment begins to work, 2.4 days during which their daily activities are restricted and 0.4 days of bed rest.

The symptoms are unpleasant — and include frequency (a desire to urinate far too frequently, and usually producing only a small volume), urgency (the sudden desire to urinate), dysuria (pain on passing urine), haematuria (blood in the urine), nocturia (having to get up at night to pass urine, which had not occurred previously), fever, and pain in the back or flanks. The later symptoms in this list are more uncommon — and more serious.

A microbiologist diagnoses a UTI by getting a 'clean catch of midstream urine', placing some on a 'culture plate', and seeing if any bacteria has grown. A diagnosis depends on having more than 100,000 bacteria per millilitre of urine — a millilitre is roughly the volume of the tip of your little finger, including the fingernail.

Causes of UTIs

There are many factors that can increase your risk of getting a UTI.

Sexual intercourse is a risk factor in both young and post-menopausal women. Low oestrogen levels is an additional risk factor for older women.

Diseases such as diabetes mellitus increase both the incidence of UTIs and the chance of complications. Kidney stones and other abnormalities, as well as spinal cord injury are also risk factors — as is pregnancy (which is definitely *not* a disease).

Genetics are also involved — if one person in a family has a history of UTIs, related women in the family then have an increased risk. Individuals who are 'non-secretors for ABO blood-group antigens' are also at greater risk for recurrent UTIs.

UTI — Pathology and Treatment

In a simple UTI, the bacteria live in the urethra (the pipe to the outside world) and the urinary bladder. In a more complicated situation, the bacteria can migrate upwards, even to the kidneys, which can sometimes become damaged.

The bacteria involved, which usually come from the bowel, are most often faecal bacteria, the well-known *E. coli* being the culprit about 80–95% of the time. Women are about 30–50 times more likely to suffer UTIs than men for a couple of reasons. In women there is a very short distance between the rectum and the opening of the urethra, and a very short length of urethra from its opening at the skin to the bladder.

Treating an acute UTI is relatively straightforward — simply take the appropriate antibiotics. However, it's more of a problem for a woman who gets recurrent UTIs. If she does nothing, she will probably get yet another UTI in the next year or so. But if she takes the antibiotics for an extended period of time, the bacteria are likely to evolve resistance to those antibiotics — and we already have enough problems with antibiotic-resistant bacteria.

Enter the Cranberry

This is where the cranberry — along with simple hygiene measures — can play a role. Indeed, the first report about the benefits of cranberry juice for bladder infections in a peer-reviewed medical journal dates back to 1914.

The cranberry is proven to be loaded with a plethora and exuberant overabundance of helpful chemicals. It carries three classes of flavonoids (flavenols, anthocyanins and proanthocyanidins), as well as catechins and triterpenoids. We are

Urinary Tract Infections

A Urinary Tract Infection (UTI) is a bacterial infection that affects any part of the urinary tract, and unfortunately they are very common in women.

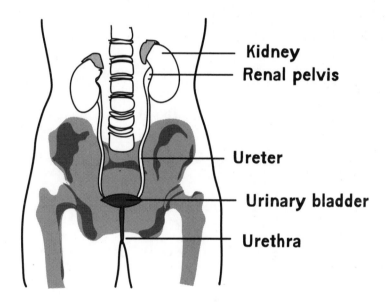

— Kidney
— Renal pelvis

— Ureter

— Urinary bladder

— Urethra

The male and female urinary tracts are relatively the same except for the length of the urethra.
(Female shown)

The symptoms of UTIs are unpleasant — they include frequency (a desire to urinate far too frequently, and usually producing only a small volume), urgency (the sudden desire to urinate), and dysuria (pain on passing urine).
It now seems that cranberry juice helps in the prevention of a recurrent UTI — but only in women.

Cranberry 101

The cranberry is a small trailing (or creeping) plant, belonging to the genus *Vaccinium*. It can creep up to 2 m in length and sprout up to 20 cm in height. It grows in the colder, wetter parts of the world, with most of the 110,000 tonne annual crop originating from the USA and Canada. The peoples of the icy far northern climes inside the Arctic Circle have made it part of their diet for thousands of years.

In the USA and Canada, it has long been consumed in pies, sauces and relishes, as a dried fruit, and as a drink.

It's called 'cranberry' in the USA because the early settlers thought it looked a little like the neck, head and beak of a crane (the bird). However, it's called 'fenberry' in the UK (a 'fen' is a marsh, its natural home).

still trying to work out what these chemicals can do for us. So far, laboratory bench studies show that they might be able to help with some cancers, some vascular and heart diseases, the bacteria that cause stomach ulcers and a reovirus that infects monkeys — but, to be sure, we need more and bigger studies in people.

These chemicals have a very neat mechanism of interfering with some of the many bacteria that can cause a UTI. They don't kill the bacteria. Instead, they seem to stop the nasty *E. coli* bacteria from adhering to the lining of the urinary bladder and urethra. This means that any *E. coli* bacteria that do make it into the lower urinary tract are very easily washed out by the regular emptying of the bladder.

A typical study looked at 150 women, all of whom had previously had a UTI. Some were given 50 ml of a cranberry-lingonberry juice concentrate to drink each day, while others (the control group) were not. Over the next six months, 39% of those in the control group suffered a UTI, while only 16% of those drinking the cranberry juice did.

It now seems that cranberry juice helps in the prevention of a recurrent UTI — but only in women. It does nothing to treat a UTI while it's flaring up — and it does nothing to help men with a UTI.

So now young lovers, wherever you are, you might think of mixing cranberry juice into your early evening cocktails … But how many prophylactics can you have in one evening?

How Much, How Often?

How much and how often should a woman take cranberry juice to reduce recurrences of a UTI? We don't really know yet.

Typically, 50–150 ml per day of pure cranberry juice seems to help. However, 100% cranberry juice is very acidic. For this reason, it is usually diluted in a cocktail of other juices to reduce the quantity to about 25%. Some studies suggest that it might be helpful to take it in two doses per day.

Paracelsus said, 'All drugs are poisons, what matters is the dose'. And even natural cranberry juice can have side effects. It can react with some regular medications — and cause kidney stones. And if you drink more than 3 litres per day (!!), you could get diarrhoea.

References

Howell, Amy B., 'Bioactive compounds in cranberries and their role in prevention of urinary tract infections', *Molecular Nutrition and Food Research*, 2007, Vol 51, Issue 6, pp 732–737.

Jepson, Ruth G., et al., 'A systematic review of the evidence for cranberries and blueberries in UTI prevention', *Molecular Nutrition and Food Research*, 2007, Vol 51, Issue 6, pp 738–745.

Kontiokari, Tero, et al., 'Randomised trial of cranberry-lingonberry juice and *Lactobacillus* GG drink for the prevention of urinary tract infections in women', *British Medical Journal*, 30 June 2001, pp 1571–1573.

Neto, Catherine C., 'Cranberry and blueberry: Evidence for protective effects against cancer and vascular disease', *Molecular Nutrition and Food Research*, 2007, Vol 51, Issue 6, pp 652–664.

They Swore it Was Tourette's

Most of us know very little about neuropsychiatric diseases. But if somebody asks us what disease makes you swear all the time, most of us will say Tourette's. And yes, there is a disease called Tourette's, but swearing is its least common presentation.

History of Tourette's Syndrome

The disease goes under many names, e.g. Tourette's, Tourette's Syndrome and Gilles de la Tourette Syndrome.

It was first noted in 1825 when the French physician Jean Marc Gaspard Itard (1775–1838) described the symptoms of ten of his patients. They found themselves performing repetitive behaviours that were not under their conscious control, including involuntary movements and verbal utterances (e.g. continually clearing their throats or saying inappropriate words).

Tourette's Syndrome is named after George Gilles de la Tourette (1859–1904), a French neurologist who wrote a paper in 1885 called 'Study of a nervous affliction'. It was based on his observations of nine patients afflicted with strange involuntary movements. At the time, Tourette was a medical resident for the famous French neurologist and physician Jean-Martin Charcot (1825–1893). It was Charcot who generously proposed that this illness be named after Tourette.

For the next century, the disease was poorly understood, and most of the treatments for it didn't really work. A major change occurred around 1970, when Drs Arthur and Elaine Shapiro described their limited successes with certain medications. They proposed that Tourette's Syndrome should henceforth be regarded as a neurological disease, not an emotional one.

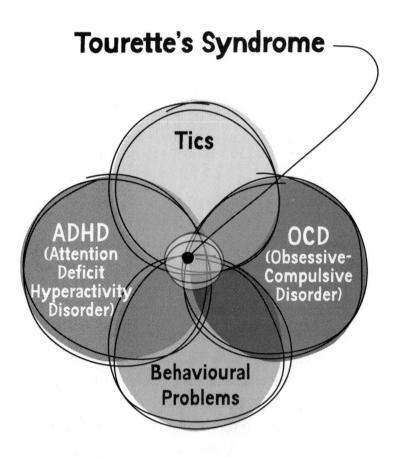

Tourette's Syndrome is known as a 'spectrum disease'. This means that it has a whole range of symptoms — from short-lived and mild, to chronic and severe.

Fancy Words

Medical vocabulary is really just a shorthand way of describing something more complex.

Some of these medical words are often used to describe Tourette's Syndrome behaviour. 'Echolalia' means 'to repeat another person's words', while 'pallalia' means 'to repeat the same words over and over'. 'Echopraxia' means 'to imitate another person's movements'. 'Coprolalia' means 'to use rude words', while 'copropraxia' means 'to make rude gestures'.

Obsessive-Compulsive Disorder has two parts. The word 'obsessive' refers to unwanted and repetitive thoughts, mental images and fears that are not related to activities of daily living. 'Compulsive' refers to the actions, which are performed to reduce the obsessive worries. Although seen as voluntary these actions are actually irresistible.

Definition of Tourette's Syndrome

Over the years, the definition of Tourette's Syndrome (TS) has changed a few times. The current definition has four parts.

First, the patient has to have several motor tics and at least one vocal tic. A 'tic' is a rapid, repeated identical movement. It can range from simple to complex — from eye-blinking or shoulder-shrugging right up to gymnastic movements such as deep knee squats and somersaults. A tic can also be vocal, involving the muscles of speech (which, of course, are controlled by the brain). Vocal tics can be as simple as a grunt or a repeated cough or clearing of the throat, or as complex as inappropriate language.

In one case, a woman, as part of her TS, uttered rude words. She became deaf from a completely separate disease and when she learnt sign language, she found herself making rude gestures when signing.

The tics are often described as a 'semi-voluntary response to an irresistible force'. It's similar to having a tickle in your throat at a symphony performance or a church service. You can refrain from having to noisily clear your throat for a while, but the longer you wait, the greater the pressure builds up, and when you do finally clear your throat, it's loud and long. Some high school students with TS say that they can suppress the tics all day at school, but once they get home, they get enormous relief from letting the tics run their course.

The second part of the definition relates to timing. The tics can happen many times per day (usually in bouts), nearly every day, or intermittently over a period greater than a year. Either way, to suit the definition, there cannot be a tic-free period longer than three months.

Third, the tics first appear at an age less than 18 years. Indeed, about half of TS sufferers have their first tic by the age of seven.

And finally, the tics are not caused by another medical condition (such as Huntington's Disease, Wilson's Disease, infectious encephalitis or Primary Dystonia) or by substance abuse.

The Numbers

At first, it was thought that TS was rare and severe. In fact, back in 1972 the US National Institute of Health estimated that there were fewer than 100 people with TS in the USA. We now know that it is relatively common and often mild.

TS occurs worldwide, in all cultures. The current estimate is that it affects 0.1–1% of the population. Males are 2–10 times more likely to be affected than females.

Depending on the study, about 40–70% of TS sufferers appear to have Attention Deficit Hyperactivity Disorder (ADHD), while 20–60% have Obsessive-Compulsive Disorder (OCD). In many cases, these conditions cause more distress to the person than the TS. The so-called Pure TS, or TS Only, the syndrome without the OCD, ADHD or other disorders, accounts for about 40% of those with TS.

In general, TS starts with simple motor tics presenting first (say, at 5–10 years of age) and the more complex motor tics later, with vocal tics developing at 8–15 years of age. TS is usually at its worst during adolescence. On average, in about two-thirds of TS sufferers, the symptoms lessen as they get older — unfortunately, in one-third, they do not.

There can be unexpected side effects. For example, if the motor tics include head-jerking, the head involvement can cause muscle strain to the neck, and even make reading very difficult.

One strange characteristic of TS is that the symptoms wax and wane, with no obvious pattern. The symptoms are unpredictable, being very different from day to day and week to week.

In general, TS does not affect life expectancy.

Other Symptoms of TS

One occasional symptom of TS is sensory hypersensitivity, e.g. a person cannot bear to wear wrinkled socks because of the extreme discomfort. Another is 'insistence on sameness' — usually associated with OCD.

Rage attacks, lasting 5–30 minutes, occasionally occur in children and teenagers.

The complex and socially inappropriate behaviour (rude words and gestures) is usually associated with ADHD.

TS in the Media

In the USA in 2001, the talkback radio doctor, Dr Laura Schlessinger, was asked about inviting a person with TS to a wedding. At the time, Dr Schlessinger was under the false impression that people with TS spent all day swearing. As part of her answer she replied: 'Well, I'm going to come to your party and just scream F-You, F-You, F-You every five seconds and see if you want to invite me back ... it is outrageous to call that a disability that should be tolerated at a wedding.' She did not realise that swearing is the least typical symptom, that only 10–15% of people exhibit it, and then for only a small fraction of the time.

TS appeared in *South Park*, in the episode called 'Le Petit Tourette'. It first went to air on 3 October 2007. In this episode, Cartman sees a little boy with Tourette's Syndrome swearing. Cartman pretends that he has TS, and enjoys being able to be as rude as he likes without getting into trouble. Things get messy when he is booked to appear on a nationwide current affairs TV show. He has a change of heart and wants to get out of it, but is threatened with murder by the host if he does. The Tourette Syndrome Association conceded that 'the episode was surprisingly well researched ... there was a surprising amount of accurate information conveyed ... providing accurate facts to the public'. *South Park* being *South Park*, they just had to use more rude words than usual and, as a result, this was their first episode to be rated at the more restrictive MA LV (i.e. mature audience, adult themes, coarse language and violence).

The Cause

At this stage, we do know that there is a very strong genetic component to the disease. It might be related to a site on Chromosome 8 (and possibly Chromosomes 5 and/or 11). There might also be a non-genetic component to TS, possibly as a reaction to being infected by a *Streptococcus* bacterium. (But, on the other hand, most people get a streptococcal infection at some stage in their early life.)

It seems that TS is a disorder of the synaptic neurotransmitter chemicals that transmit information in the nervous system. Scanning studies of the brains of TS sufferers show extra activity in those parts of the brain dealing with sensation, movement and language.

To summarise, we don't really know the cause(s) of TS. This is partly because the brain is fiendishly complex. Another reason is that we have very few animal models to compare and study, apart from some stallions with inherited repetitive grooming rituals and some Labrador dogs that will lick their paws until they are abraded.

But we know that the risk factors include having a family history of TS, being male and under the age of 20 years.

Famous TS Sufferers

TS is known as a 'spectrum disease'. This means that it has a whole range of symptoms — from short-lived and mild to chronic and severe (fortunately, this is relatively uncommon). Therefore, some people with milder symptoms can disguise it in their daily lives.

Unfortunately, some cannot. Dr Samuel Johnson (1709–1784), the writer, critic and poet, who wrote the first modern dictionary of the English Language, had TS. His biographer, James Boswell, wrote that Dr Johnson had 'nervous movements' and would often continually repeat fragments of words or other sounds. He would suppress these tics with a great effort of his will, as he was much embarrassed by them.

In recent times, the actor Dan Aykroyd claimed in a radio interview that he had mild TS. Athletes and musicians have also claimed that they have tamed the restless energy and spontaneity of TS to their own advantage.

A few studies have shown that people with TS can have a higher IQ and quicker motor activity than expected. The famed neurologist and author, Dr Oliver Sacks, writes that while 'one must not romanticise Tourette's … one may have the rather rare situation of a biological condition becoming creative or becoming an integral part of the identity and creativity of an individual'.

Rarely Rude

The florid symptoms that most people believe to be typical of Tourette's Syndrome are actually the *least* typical. This is probably because they get all the attention. The majority of people diagnosed with TS will never do anything rude. The obscene words and rude gestures appear in only 10–15% of people with TS, and then only for a very small fraction of the day.

The rest of the time, people with TS are just like anybody else — I swear.

References

Kushner, Howard I., *A Cursing Brain? The Histories of Tourette Syndrome*, Cambridge, Massachusetts: Harvard University Press, 1999.

Pearce, J.M.S., 'Doctor Samuel Johnson: "the great convulsionary" a victim of Gilles de la Tourette's syndrome', *Journal of The Royal Society of Medicine*, 1994, Vol 87, No 7, pp 396, 397.

Sacks, Oliver, 'Tourette's syndrome and creativity: Exploiting the ticcy witticisms and witty ticcicisms', *British Medical Journal*, 19–26 December 1992, pp 1515–1516.

Moth to a Flame
(Let Bogongs be Bogongs)

You hear the phrase all the time, '… drawn like a moth to the flame'. And you've probably witnessed it. It's a hot summer evening, you're on the verandah when you suddenly notice a moth zooming towards the light. But although the moth appears to be attracted to the light, it's actually just confused by it.

Moth Facts

The wingspans of moths range in size from a tiny 4 mm to a terrifying 300 mm. Moths are closely related to butterflies. They have a similar life cycle — egg, larva (caterpillar), pupa (chrysalis) and, finally, the imago (adult). Moths tend to be nocturnal, but there are a few species that are active at dawn and dusk and others that are active during the day.

Beneficial or a Menace?

Moths and people certainly have a love-hate relationship.

The silkworm (the larva of some moth species) makes raw silk to build its cocoon. Farming silkworms for their silk has been occurring for hundreds of years. And we use about 130,000 tonnes of this raw silk each year to make beautiful soft fabrics.

Eating the larva or caterpillar of the Mopane Moth (*Gonimbrasia belina*) is popular in southern Africa, as was eating the larva of the Bogong Moth (*Agrotis infusa*) in the Australian Alps. Indigenous Australians would roast the bodies in hot ashes to burn off the legs and wings. What remained would then be mashed into a meal that has a nutty taste, like walnuts.

On the other hand, various species of moths attack and destroy crops and trees around the world. However, many moths provide a beneficial service by pollinating some wild plants that might otherwise not survive.

Short and Happy Life

The eggs of the Bogong Moth start their life cycle on the black soil plains of the Darling Downs in Southeast Queensland, west of the Great Dividing Range.

The eggs hatch into larvae/cutworm caterpillars in early spring. They dig a burrow in the dirt at the base of a plant, hide in it by day and come out at night to eat the plant. Once they are about 5 cm long, they pupate in a cocoon inside their burrow, emerging as adult moths 3–4 weeks later.

These black soil plains get too hot for the moths in summer. So when the summer storms herald their arrival with atmospheric low pressure systems, the moths take to the wing in their billions. They can flap a few hundred kilometres south each night, keeping up their strength by feeding on flowering gum trees. When the Sun comes up, they dive down to find a safe resting spot that is both dark and cool to hide in until sunset. So, in this case, the lights of a big city can trick them into landing before they should.

The journey can be fraught with natural disasters as well. Winds have been known to blow them as far off course as Melbourne and New Zealand. After flapping some 800 km along the east coast of Australia, they arrive at their cool resting place in the caves across the high Bogong Plains near Mount Bogong which (of course) is in the Bogong National Park in the Australian Alps.

Over the summer they 'sleep' in these caves — 'estivation' is the insect equivalent of animal hibernation — with about 27,000 moths squashed onto each square metre of the cave walls.

After sunlight, these moths make up the second largest input of energy into the Australian Alps in summer. It's almost 'Meals on Wheels' for the local animals, with all this wonderful food at their doorstep. These predators include birds (e.g. pippets, robins and ravens), spiders, reptiles, fish, mammals (especially foxes) and marsupials (e.g. the Antechinus and the Mountain Pigmy Possum).

Around February and March, they head for home. Only one in every thousand gets back there to mate. Then, after a short life with lots of travel (about 1,500 km), they die.

Tricky Flight Path

So what's the story with moths dive-bombing the verandah?

You have to look carefully to notice this, but most of their flight path is not straight, but curved. Moths, like other nocturnal travellers, use quite a sophisticated system of Celestial Navigation to find their way. It's called 'Transverse Orientation' — keeping a fixed

Like a moth to a flame...

The wingspans of moths range in size from a tiny 4 mm to a terrifying 300 mm.

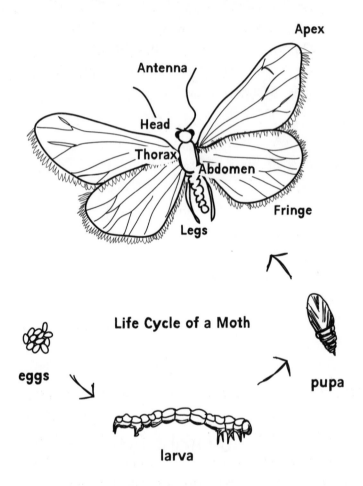

Apex

Antenna

Head

Thorax

Abdomen

Legs

Fringe

Life Cycle of a Moth

eggs

larva

pupa

Moths are closely related to butterflies.
They have a similar life cycle —
egg, larva (caterpillar),
pupa (chrysalis) and, finally, the imago (adult).

angle on a distant source of light. And it is remarkably effective.

Suppose that the Moon is high in the northern sky, and that you want to head west for a few hours. Easy, just keep the Moon on your right (the north) and you will automatically be heading west. It works only because the Moon is so far away.

Now try navigating, not with the Moon but with a streetlight only a few metres away. When you try to keep it on your right, you will very quickly find yourself walking in a circle. And if you keep the streetlight somewhere between directly to your right and directly in front of you, you will quickly enter a death spiral and hit the post of the streetlight. This is how the moths get tricked.

Although moths have been around for many millions of years, they don't have much evolutionary history in dealing with bright city lights at night. In Australia, the Bogong Moths leave hot Southeast Queensland every summer and flap their way about 800 km south to arrive in the cool Australian Alps in November. But the city of Canberra has blossomed into existence along their ancestral pathway. The moths get tricked by the city lights, become disoriented and head for the lights of buildings in Canberra.

Trick Lights

It's not only moths that get tricked by lights. Some baby sea turtles get tricked also. Their evolutionary imperative is that, when they hatch on shore and dig up through the sand to the surface, they head in the direction of the Moon. They hatch at night when the Moon is over the sea — which is the right direction for the baby turtles to scramble towards. However, because we humans have placed lights along the beach, some baby turtles head inland towards the lights — and die.

Moths Carry Arsenic

Bogong Moths are poisoning their summer home in the Australian Alps with arsenic that they gather from Southeast Queensland. The arsenic was brought to our attention when local scientists in the Australian Alps noticed that all plant life was dead for 30 m on the downhill side of the caves in which the Bogong Moths sleep during the summer months.

The story began in the 1920s when vast amounts of arsenic were used, not only to kill the invasive prickly pear cactus but also in general agricultural sprays. The local environment took up this arsenic.

Polluting chemicals are usually carried by wind or water or, as in this case, up the food chain. The Bogong Moths pick up the arsenic from the soil and plants when they are young and growing. On average, there is one Bogong larva in each 10 m² of soil. They then carry this arsenic in their bodies into the caves where their density can reach 27,000 moths per square metre.

The arsenic then enters the alpine food chain in many ways. The Bogong Moths are eaten, transferring the arsenic to a range of predators. For example, the local feral foxes eat about half-a-billion moths each year. The moths defecate, dumping the arsenic-rich faeces on the ground, the rain then spreading it around. The moths also die. In some caves, the moth corpses are 1.5 m thick on the floor.

Flaming Beauty

But perhaps it's all part of Nature's Grand Plan. In 'The lesson of the moth', in *Archy and Mehitabel* by Don Marquis, Archy (a journalist reincarnated as a cockroach) spoke with a moth who knew it was going to die. There are many ways to die but, said the moth, 'it is better to be happy for a moment and be burned up with beauty'.

Reference

Marquis, Don, *Archy and Mehitabel,* New York: New York, Anchor Books, published by Doubleday; copyright 1927, 1930, Anchor Books edition 1973, 1990.

Runner's High

There are some people who invest in kilojoules so they can store them carefully around their middle. And there are those who invest in physical fitness, which they build up by pounding the pavement. And while the Slouches on Couches expound the virtues of watching TV or lazing under a tree reading a book, the runners pant breathlessly of their secret reward — the Runner's High.

Now here's something odd. Runners have always confidently claimed that the Runner's High is due to chemicals called 'endorphins' released by the brain. Although there was nothing approaching real proof for this claim until February 2008, people still believed in it wholeheartedly.

How the Myth Began

Opiate drugs (e.g. opium, morphine, codeine and heroin) affect the human brain because brain cells have receptors for these drugs. This is how our brains recognise these opiates (or, indeed, how any of the cells in the body recognise any chemicals). So, on one hand, there are chemicals that you can extract from a pretty poppy that originally grew in Turkey. And, on the other hand, human brains *all over the world* have receptors for these chemicals. But why should there be a link? The search for endorphins began with this deceptively simple question.

In the mid-1970s, we finally found the answer. The brain makes its own opiates that are similar to the opiates found in the Opium Poppy. Some of them were called 'endorphins' — short for 'endogenous morphines', i.e. 'chemicals like morphine' that are 'made in the body'.

Brain Opiates

There are three main groups of opiates that the human brain makes, each coming from different precursor chemicals. They each have variable effects on the different natural opiate receptors, which include k-receptors (kappa), m-receptors (mu), d-receptors (delta) and s-receptors (sigma). These receptors are found in varying degrees in different parts of the brain.

The 'enkephalins' (which means 'in the head') were the first natural opiates to be classified as acting on the brain. They are a breakdown product of, and come from, 'proenkephalin'. They appear widely in the central and peripheral nervous systems and also in the adrenal medulla. They cause respiratory depression and reduced gastrointestinal motility.

The 'dynorphins' are another class of natural opiates. There are several types, including A-dynorphin and B-dynorphin. They come from 'prodynorphin' and act mainly on k-receptors on cells. They act as painkillers and antidepressants and cause physical dependence.

Finally we have the class that everybody has heard of — the 'endorphins'. These come from 'pro-opiomelanocortin'. Again, there are several types, including beta-endorphins, which are excellent at giving spinal-pain relief.

Running happy ...

'Runner's High' is said to occur when strenuous exercise takes a person over a threshold that activates endorphin production.

The Brain

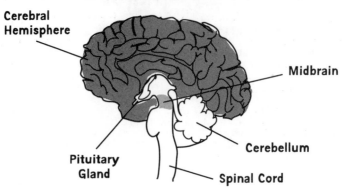

Cerebral Hemisphere

Midbrain

Cerebellum

Pituitary Gland

Spinal Cord

Endorphins are produced by the pituitary gland.

Activation of opiate receptors by endorphins regulate many functions within the body, including pain perception, internal temperature, appetite, sexual behaviour and blood pressure.

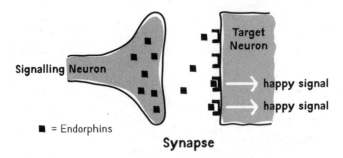

Signalling Neuron

Target Neuron

happy signal

happy signal

■ = Endorphins

Synapse

A synapse is a small gap between neurons where nerve impulses pass between nerve cells.

And the link to the Runner's High? Well, fit people supposedly enjoy boundless energy, a zest for life and reduced stress. But the Runner's High is something even better again. It differs considerably between individuals, but it's described as a drug-like, elusive feeling of euphoria. It encompasses weightlessness, inner harmony, feelings of disembodiment, a total lack of anxiety or stress and, sometimes, even the occasional orgasmic sensation. In other words, it's much better than the euphoria you feel from opening a packet of chocolate bikkies. Under the influence of the Runner's High, some runners have even been reduced to tears at the sight of a cute puppy.

Runners began to whisper to each other about this high when jogging began to become popular in the mid-1970s. It was around this time that endorphins were discovered, so it seemed obvious that endorphins caused the high — but there was no proof.

Chinese War on Opium

Arabian traders introduced opium to China somewhere around 600 AD. In 1860, China was forced to tolerate the legalisation of opium, after losing the two Opium Wars (of 1839–1842 and 1856–1860) with Britain (which held a monopoly on the sale of opium in Asia). As a consequence, by 1906 China consumed 39,000 tonnes of the world's total opium production of 41,000 tonnes. About one-quarter of China's adult male population (some 13.5 million) was addicted to the stuff.

Poppy Seeds

Poppy seeds can give you a false positive for opiates in a drug screen.

Poppy seeds are commonly used as a flavouring and topping for cakes and breads. Typically, 1 g of poppy seeds carries up to 33 millionths of a gram of morphine and 14 millionths of a gram of codeine. Although these are very small quantities, modern technology can easily detect even smaller amounts.

Before 30 November 1998, the US Substance Abuse and Mental Health Services Administration had a cutoff level of 300 billionths of a gram per millilitre of urine. Two poppy seed rolls (containing 1.5 g of poppy seeds) were enough to trigger an alert. So in 1998, the cutoff level was lifted to 2,000 billionths of a gram per millilitre of urine.

The Original Morphine

Endorphins are a family of chemicals that have effects similar to morphine — except that they are made in the body. So let's look at the source of the original opiates — the Opium Poppy.

There are about 50 different species of the poppy, scientifically called *Papaver somniferum*. They usually have nodding buds on a single stem, four to six flowers with petals, and grow between 1–5 m high. They include the Oriental, the Shirley, the Long-headed and, yes, the Opium Poppy. If you cut the central bulb of the poppy with a sharp blade, it will exude a soft milky sap that will harden overnight into a rubbery latex. This latex contains up to 16% morphine.

We don't know why the Opium Poppy makes opiates. Perhaps they are a waste product, or a protective mechanism or a part of the ripening process.

The painkilling properties of the latex from the Opium Poppy have been known for millennia. Its seeds have been found in Spanish caves dating back to 4200 BC. By 3400 BC, the Sumerians were calling it *Hul Gil*, or 'joy plant'. The ancient Egyptian medical textbook known as the *Ebers Papyrus*, written around 1500 BC, listed the latex of the Opium Poppy as a painkiller. The ancient Greeks, Romans and Persians also knew this plant well for its painkilling properties.

Opiates tend to act in one of two locations — on the central nervous system or on smooth muscle. They can relieve the pain of kidney stones and gallstones by reducing the contractility of the smooth muscle in the ducts. They can reduce a cough and relieve respiratory distress by acting on the central nervous system. They can treat diarrhoea by reducing fluid loss and relaxing the smooth muscles of the gut.

Use of Opiates

For many thousands of years, opium was the only painkiller known to medicine. When it was mixed with alcohol, it was called 'laudanum', which was very popular in Europe. And 'paregoric' was a camphorated solution of opium, used to treat diarrhoea by relaxing the smooth muscle of the gut.

Morphine was first extracted from opium in 1804, and codeine in 1832. However, heroin was obtained around 1898, by treating morphine with acetic anhydride.

Various synthetic opiates were first synthesised in the late 1930s. These include methadone and meperidine.

Discovery of Human Opiates

It was in 1960 that Choh Hao Li, a neurologist at the University of California, San Francisco, first isolated beta-endorphin. He purified it from the pituitary glands of 500 camels. But because this chemical didn't answer the questions he was asking, he did no further work with it. (Much later, after other workers had announced their discoveries, Li went back to his original beta-endorphin. When used as a painkiller and compared to morphine, he found that it was three times more powerful when injected into the veins and 48 times more powerful when injected directly into the brain.)

By 1973 other workers had worked out that various animal brains had receptors that interacted weakly with opiates, such as morphine.

However, it was in 1975, that John Hughes and Hans Kosterlitz isolated some opiate-like chemicals from the brains of pigs. Because these chemicals were found in the head, they called them 'enkephalins'. On a chemical level, they are all made from five amino acids stuck together to make a protein. There are two types of enkephalins — one with the amino acid 'leucine', the other with the amino acid 'methionine'. Although quite addictive, they were weak at killing pain — unfortunately, the exact opposite of the result that everybody wanted.

Endorphins are Discovered

A few studies in the 1980s found endorphins in the bloodstream of people who had been running. However, there were a few problems with these studies.

First, they measured endorphins in the blood, not in the brain. So these endorphins could have been produced anywhere in the body as part of a gross stress response. Second, the levels of circulating endorphins did not relate to the level of 'being high' that the runners experienced.

And finally, because we are talking about the human body, the bland claim that 'endorphins give you the Runner's High' is too simplistic. For one thing, the human body makes several types of opiates — endorphins are just one of them. For another, there are many types of opiate receptors that your natural opiates affect in differing degrees — and some of these opiates can make you feel unhappy or even sick. This might explain why, after a decent run, some runners feel like vomiting, rather than being 'at one with the Godhead' around them.

But the high was definitely real for many. Some people with Obsessive-Compulsive Disorder actually became 'addicted' to their regular dose of exercise. Indeed, some people use exercise as a coping mechanism — and provided that they don't actually exercise so much that they injure themselves, it is probably perfectly fine.

Opium Production

In 1980, the world's production of legal and illegal opium was about 2,000 tonnes. By 2002 it had increased to 5,000 tonnes, with Afghanistan the world's leading producer. (Production decreased in 2001 when the Taliban placed a ban on the growing of Opium Poppies the previous year.) And by 2008, opium production in Afghanistan had increased enormously, thanks to the ongoing war against the Taliban. Afghan farmers can make much more money growing Opium Poppies than any other crop.

The Proof ...

In February 2008, the neurologist Dr H. Boecker published his paper on the Runner's High. His team in Germany measured both 'euphoria' and whether brain opiates were binding to various receptors in the brains of ten distance runners. The runners in the study were deliberately not told what the researchers were looking for. Typically, they were running 21.5 km in 115 minutes at an average speed of 11 kph, with their hearts beating at 144 beats per minute, compared to their regular 52 beats. The intensity of this long and continuous work-out forced the muscles to use up their stored glycogen. (Sports such as swimming, cross-country skiing and cycling produce the same effects.)

The study produced two findings. First, that the natural opiates were binding to those parts of the brain that deal with mood. Second, that there was a direct relationship between the euphoria and how the natural opiates were binding to the brain. Dr Boecker said in *The New York Times*: 'You could really see the difference after two hours of running. You could see it in their faces.'

Are the natural opiates endorphins? Probably. Mind you, it was a very small sample size.

So, in this case, the claim that brain opiates cause the Runner's High is probably true. But it took us one-third of a century to prove it.

References

Boecker, H., et al., 'The Runner's High: Opiodergic mechanisms in the human brain', *Cerebral Cortex*, 21 February 2008.

Hughes, J., et al., 'Identification of two related pentapeptides from the brain, with potent opiate agonist activity', *Nature*, 18 December 1975, pp 577–579.

Kolata, Gina, 'Yes, running can make you high', *The New York Times*, 27 March 2008.

Simantov, R., et al., 'Morphine-like peptides in mammalian brain: Isolation, structure elucidation, and interactions with the opiate receptor', *Proceedings of the National Academy of Sciences*, July 1976, Vol 73, Issue 7, pp 2515–2519.

Is This On, Mike?

I do a bit of speaking at universities, conferences and public meetings and have come to know the audiovisual (AV) people quite well. They have told me how a few common mythconceptions about microphones make their job hard.

There are two myths. One, the way to test a microphone is to tap it firmly with the fingers. Two, microphones will magically 'reach out' and amplify only the speaker's voice, no matter how quietly they speak.

Microphone 101

The word 'microphone' comes from the Greek words *mikros* meaning 'small' and *phone* meaning 'voice' or 'sound'.

One of the first appearances of the word was in a 1683 dictionary, where it was defined as 'an instrument by which small sounds are intensified'. Of course, this referred to non-electronic devices, such as megaphones and ear trumpets.

The first 'modern' microphones appeared in the 1870s. In one early version, the person's voice came in through a funnel, landing on a stretched membrane of thin metal, which then vibrated. This membrane was attached to a sharp needle, which scratched a pattern into thin metal foil. You could also run this system backwards. In this case, when the needle ran over the foil, the membrane vibrated, allowing you to hear a rough version of the original sound.

Today, most microphones rely on the speaker's voice setting off pressure waves in the air, which then land on a diaphragm. In the popular dynamic microphone (which often looks like an ice-cream cone), the diaphragm is attached to a ring-shaped coil of thin wires. The coil is either inside a hollow magnet or has a magnet inside it. Either way, when the diaphragm moves relative to the magnet, electricity flows through the wires of the coil. This electricity is then amplified and pumped out through the loudspeakers.

Public Speaking 101

The human brain is highly proficient at listening to a specific source in a noisy environment. It can filter out all the unwanted noise and bring into the foreground the sounds that you are concentrating on, such as another person's conversation in a crowded room.

However, our current technology — the combination of a microphone and an amplifier — has not yet been able to do this. Today's mike and amp will make everything louder — both the unwanted background noise and the signal that you want.

If you speak softly into the microphone (which is what most people do), the mike technician has to crank up the volume on the amplifier. Although this will make your voice loud enough for the audience to hear, unfortunately it will also make the background noise louder. The audience will notice this unwanted, amplified noise.

But if you speak more loudly, the mike technician can reduce the overall volume. With the amplifier turned down the background noise will be reduced. But the audience will still hear you clearly, because you are speaking more loudly.

Testing ... One, Two, Three

The word 'microphone' comes from the Greek language
— 'micros' means small, and 'phone' means voice.

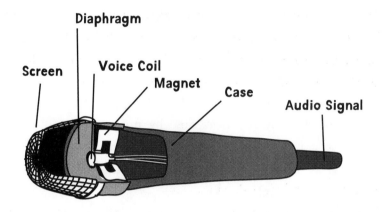

Diaphragm

Screen

Voice Coil

Magnet

Case

Audio Signal

Microphones convert acoustical energy (sound waves)
into electrical energy (the audio signal).

Cross-section of a dynamic mike

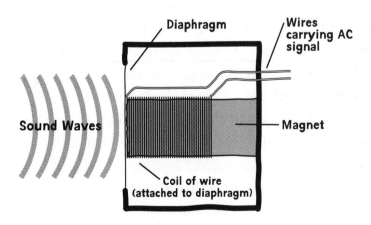

Diaphragm

Wires carrying AC signal

Sound Waves

Magnet

Coil of wire
(attached to diaphragm)

Mike Myths

The first of the two myths claims that the way to test whether a microphone is working is to tap it firmly.

Unfortunately, the diaphragm inside a mike is delicate. It is designed to move in response to tiny variations in air pressure. Therefore, a solid thump can sometimes knock the delicate internal mechanisms out of place. At the very least, you will inject a sharp audio 'spike' through the entire audio chain from the microphone to the amplifier and the loudspeakers. This 'spike' has been known to cause damage.

The microphone is a device that is supposed to help amplify speech — its only function. So why not test this function by simply speaking into it? AV technicians often tell me that they are bemused as to why a speaker thinks that the only way to test a mike is to hit it firmly.

The second myth claims that you do not have to speak loudly into a microphone.

People believe that the mike will somehow magically 'reach out' and amplify only their voice. So widespread is this belief that most people will actually speak more softly than normal into a mike.

And when they hear their own amplified voice coming through the loudspeakers, they do not see this as a sign of success — which it is. Instead, they will deliberately speak more softly and/or move their mouth away from the mike, until they can no longer hear themselves.

The AV technicians at the back of the hall are now left with only one option — to increase the amplification of the microphone circuit. The microphone will now pick up the faint mouse-like whimperings of the speaker — as well as the speaker's own voice coming through the loudspeakers. This can then set off the squeal of the dreaded 'feedback loop'. In response, most speakers will talk even more quietly. And the AV technicians at the back of the hall get even more annoyed, because the audience now blames them and not the poor microphone technique of the speaker, for the bad sound.

My Mike Technique

I usually use a lapel mike (in my shirt). This leaves my hands free to operate the laser pointer and the remote control for the presentation. If I were to turn my head to one side or the other, I would go 'off mike', so I am careful to turn my head and shoulders as one unit.

I always ask for a new battery (even so, I have had a battery die on me a few times, when the technicians have told me that a new battery has been installed, but wasn't). I am a stage walker (i.e. I don't stand still at a lectern). So before a presentation I walk around the stage to see if there are locations to avoid because of possible feedback. I also test the mike by speaking at the loudest and softest levels I will use on stage, so that the technicians can set the levels correctly. And, of course, I always run the cable inside my shirt — for a more professional look.

The Cure

I have been present at practice sessions when the AV technicians have come onto the stage and asked the presenter to speak more loudly. The presenter then continues to speak at exactly the same volume. For some unknown reason, they seem to have a real reluctance to speaking loudly. But this is exactly what actors do on stage — they 'project' their voices. I saw one technician use a neat trick to get the presenter to speak more loudly. She would say, 'Imagine that your child is drowning in a river, and that you want to call for help. Now start calling for help.' In many cases, this simple exercise would open the floodgates, the presenter then beginning to speak more loudly.

So next time you're on stage, get close to the microphone, don't tap it, speak loudly — and the only feedback you'll get will be applause.

Roadie for Bo Diddley

I spent a few years as a roadie for a few bands in Sydney. This involved loading the speakers and amps into the van, setting them up at the gig, wiring it all up, and then 'bumping out' at the end of the gig. One of these bands, Wasted Daze, was invited to be the backing band for Bo Diddley (the blues musician) for two of his Australian tours.

So that's how I became a roadie for Bo.

Reference

Nisbett, Alec, *The Use of Microphones*, London: Focal Press, 1983.

Crash Collider: LHC Destroys Universe

Back in the Old Days, before terrorists and tsunamis were blamed for trying to destroy the Earth, it was the labcoat-wearing, mostly bald (apart from two tufts of hair), certifiably mad and totally friendless Mad Scientists who were going to do it with one of their crazy experiments. No surprise, but scientists are back in the firing line.

Terrifyingly, this time scientists are being accused of trying to blow up the Universe. The firing up of the Large Hadron Collider (LHC) in Europe has also fired up a groundswell of paranoia against this science experiment that will supposedly unleash uncontrollable forces, wreck the planet and kill us all — and a few moments later, destroy the entire Universe as well.

There are three specific doomsday claims — that the wacky scientists will accidentally make a Black Hole that will swallow the Earth, or that they will collapse the Universe into a weird quantum vacuum, or that they will convert all the matter in the Universe into 'strange' matter.

But what is the LHC and why are the doomsayers wrong?

What is the LHC?

The Large Hadron Collider (LHC) was built to help answer some Big Questions in Particle Physics. It has taken over 20 years, and scientists and engineers from over 60 countries, to build, and is designed to recreate some of the titanic energies found in the Universe immediately after the Big Bang.

The largest and most powerful collider ever built, it is located inside a huge, specially constructed underground tunnel, shaped like a ring, which straddles the borders of Switzerland and France.

The LHC will generate so much raw data that if it were stored on CDs, the stack would reach the Moon in six months. The project will employ about half of all the particle physicists in the world.

Particle Physics 101

It has been said that Particle Physics is like throwing two watches at each other at high speed, and then trying to work out how a watch works by looking at the various bits that come flying out. Trying to understand what everything is made of has bothered thinkers and scientists for thousands of years.

In 1915, Ernest Rutherford, the New Zealand-born scientist, fired charged helium atoms (alpha particles) at a sheet of very thin gold foil. The thinking at the time was that matter was made from large solid atoms, so matter was like large solid plums (the atoms) richly scattered through a pudding (the stuff in between). Rutherford expected the helium atoms to go through the foil, and that they would all be slightly deflected at a small angle, as they hit the atoms in the foil. Instead, most of the alpha particles went straight through the foil, totally unaffected — but were deflected at more than 90°. He later said: 'It was almost as incredible as if you fired a fifteen-inch [38 cm] shell at a piece of tissue paper and it came back and hit you.'

He had discovered that atoms were mostly empty space, with tiny solid cores. The atom is kind of like a tiny solar system, with the nucleus at the centre and electrons orbiting around it.

Then it was discovered that the nucleus itself is made of protons and neutrons.

Then it was discovered that the protons and neutrons were made from 'quarks' and gluons.

And now we have the Large Hadron Collider ...

What LHC Does

The LHC collides together two beams of protons, i.e. hadrons, that are travelling in opposite directions. 'Hadrons' are subatomic particles (such as the protons or neutrons in the core of an atom) that interact with each other strongly.

The 300 trillion protons in each beam travel at 99.99991% of the speed of light through skinny pipes just 5 cm in diameter. These tiny pipes are inside cylinders full of wiring, electronics and magnets. The cylinders are arranged in a circle 27 km in circumference, and are buried 50–100 m underground. At that speed, all of the speeding protons put together have the energy of an express train.

The protons orbit the ring about 11,000 times each second. The protons would travel in a straight line, except for the 1,200 superpowerful magnets which force them to take a curved path. These are not ordinary magnets — they each weigh several tonnes, and make up the largest array of superconducting magnets ever built. To keep the magnets in the superconducting mode, they are cooled by 130 tonnes of liquid helium. The liquid helium is colder than the temperature of deep Space.

This kind of high-energy physics can be hazardous. If a loose nut or screw is left lying around when one of these magnets is switched on, it will smash into the magnet with the speed of a bullet and destroy it. On the other hand, if any of the magnets fail, the proton beam will stop following the curve of the pipes and burn through the pipe wall. The energy in the beam is the same as in 157 kg of TNT — you wouldn't want to be near the beam if it punched its way out of its tiny pipe! The energy stored in the magnets is even greater — the same as in 2.5 tonnes of TNT.

Once the beam has been switched on, it runs for ten hours before needing to be topped up. In that time, the protons cover a distance equal to a round trip to the planet Neptune and back.

For most of the tunnel, the two proton beams are kept parallel and separate. But there are four crossing points where the beams hit each other. This is where the collisions happen — some 600 million of them each second. If any human beings were near the crossing points when the proton beams were running, they would die very quickly from the radiation.

Large = Enormous

The LHC has four main collision detectors. Over 2,500 scientists laboured to build just one of its four detectors — which, by itself, has more iron in it than the Eiffel Tower.

These 'detectors' aren't small devices sitting on a benchtop, like those used in the early days of Particle Physics. Each one is about

Catch the Fireball

One of the detectors, called LHCb, is run by about 663 scientists. It has a fairly specific goal — to study the subtle differences between matter and antimatter. When the Universe popped into existence with the Big Bang, it had equal amounts of both. But now the Universe is made just of matter. Why? How? LHCb might help us answer these questions.

Another detector, ALICE, also has a quite specific goal. It studies the quark-gluon plasma, by smashing together the nuclei of lead atoms.

The other two detectors, ATLAS and CMS are more general. They catch and measure everything coming out of the collisions.

the size of a multi-storey building, wrapped around the collision zone, and costing up to several hundred million dollars.

There are four separate detectors, so there are four collision zones or crossing points. The detectors have been built by separate teams, and work both independently of each other, and together.

The collisions at these crossing points produce a primordial fireball, which then cools down into various subatomic particles, which then are caught by the detectors. Hopefully, the products of the collisions will include the long-sought Higgs Particle, which is thought to endow everything in the Universe with the strange property that we call 'mass'.

When Science or Technology is very advanced, it becomes Art. One of the theorists at the European Organization for Nuclear Research (known as CERN) calls these detectors 'sunken cathedrals'.

The (Really) Large Hadron Collider

Location: Border of France and Switzerland
LHC Circumference: 27.5 kilometres approx.

The countryside near Geneva is home to the
world's most massive physics experiment.

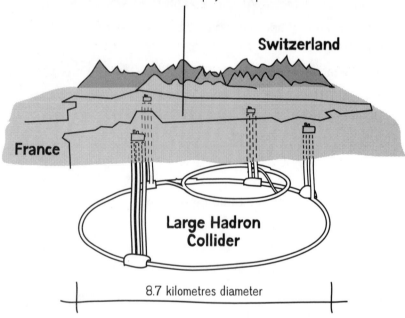

Switzerland

France

Large Hadron
Collider

8.7 kilometres diameter

Inside the LHC, insanely big and powerful magnets that have
been chilled to a few degrees above absolute zero, will shoot
beams of superenergetic protons and lead nuclei in a loop
at incredibly high speeds. The speeds reached are
close to the speed of light and when the protons collide
head-on they will replicate conditions that existed mere
moments after the Big Bang.

ATLAS vs CMS

ATLAS weighs 7,000 tonnes, and is run by 1,800 scientists from 34 countries. It is both larger and lighter than CMS — so light that if you wrapped it in plastic sheeting, it would float on water. It's about 45 m long and 25 m high, and would half fill the Cathedral of Notre Dame in Paris.

CMS stands for Compact Muon Solenoid — but obviously the scientists were having a little joke when they called it 'compact'. It weighs 12,500 tonnes, and is 15 m high and 23 m long. It takes about 2,500 scientists from 37 countries and 155 scientific institutions to run it. This is the one that has more iron in it than the Eiffel Tower. At the very heart of the CMS is a camera that photographs the particles erupting out from the primeval fireball — but what a camera! It has a 60 megapixel chip, and can take 40 million pictures each second (that's right, not 40 but 40 million).

The Higgs Particle

You've probably heard that mass and energy can be turned into each other. In a nuclear weapon, a small amount of mass is turned into a huge amount of energy. In the collisions in the LHC, the opposite happens — energy is turned into mass. In a bizarre example of how mass and energy can be interchanged, two small, fast-moving protons will collide to make much heavier slower particles — like two nippy light planes colliding to make a lumbering bus. The energy of the speeding protons will hopefully be converted to the mass of the Higgs Particle — the Holy Grail of Particle Physics. It is supposed to endow 'stuff' with this weird property called 'mass'.

According to the best theories that the scientists have, the Big Bang happened about 13–14 billion years ago. Back in the beginning, the basic elementary particles that all matter is made from did not have any mass. But they then acquired their mass by pushing their way through a strange thick 'mud' that is part of the Fabric of Space-Time. This gloopy sticky 'mud' is called the 'Higgs Field'. It manifests itself as the hypothetical Higgs Particle, named after the Scottish physicist Peter Higgs. He first discussed this proposition back in 1964.

But how do you explain this complicated stuff in plain English? This was the problem that William Waldegrave, the British Science Minister, had in 1993, so he offered prizes to anybody who could explain this concept on a single A4 sheet of paper. A total of 125 scientists entered the competition, and Minister Waldegrave awarded prizes (bottles of champagne) to five of them.

The winning entry was proposed by David Miller, a physicist from University College London. He compared the Higgs Field to a cocktail party made up of Tory party members, all of whom love Margaret Thatcher enormously.

Margaret Thatcher enters the room alone (i.e. she begins with no mass). As she crosses the room, Tory party members attach themselves in loving adoration of her (i.e. they give her 'mass').

So the Higgs Field imparts a drag to any matter passing through it, giving it 'mass'. Unlike other fields (e.g. gravity, electric, magnetic), the Higgs Field has exactly the same value throughout the Universe. What varies is how different particles interact with it.

Hopefully the LHC will find the Higgs Particle in its brief lifetime of 10^{-24} seconds, during which it will travel 10^{-15} m before it breaks apart.

Particle Spin-Off

One useful thing that has emerged from the work of particle physicists is the World Wide Web. By the way, the World Wide Web is *not* the internet. The World Wide Web is the software that lets you use the internet.

The Center for Nuclear Energy Research (CERN) in Europe, which has run various Colliders, is now running the LHC. (Note: CERN is the European Organization for Nuclear Research. It's name is derived from the acronym for the French Conseil Européen pour la Recerche Nucléaire.) Back in 1990, CERN was the largest internet node in Europe. In those days, only scientists used the internet, and then only as a way to communicate and share data among themselves. Tim Berners-Lee was a computer scientist at CERN. On 25 December 1990, he set up the very first successful link between an HTTP (Hyper Text Transfer Protocol) and a server across the internet. The World Wide Web was born.

So the World Wide Web is a useful spin-off from Particle Physics.

End of Everything

So just how will the LHC cause the End of Everything? The claims against the LHC fit into the Really Big Problem basket, so let me deal with them one at a time.

Doom 1: Black Hole (Part 1)

There are people who claim that the LHC will create a Black Hole, which will then gobble up our planet.

But there are two reasons why you don't have to worry about the LHC making Black Holes. First, it's probably theoretically impossible to make them and, second, if we could make them they would be incredibly tiny and would evaporate in a time too short to measure with our current technology.

In reality, the LHC simply does not have enough grunt to create a Black Hole.

Let me explain. The smallest possible length in our Universe is probably (let me emphasise *probably*) the so-called Planck Length. According to various theories, any distance or object smaller than this is lost in a bubbling sea of quantum vacuum (more about this later).

So, therefore, the smallest possible Black Hole is the size of this Planck Length, which is about 1.6×10^{-35}m. OK so far?

Theory tells us that a Black Hole of this size (i.e. 1.6×10^{-35}m) would have a mass of ten millionths of a gram. To create this much mass with a collider would need energies of 10^{16} TeV (a TeV is a unit of energy equal to one trillion electron volts) — but the LHC can generate only 14 TeV. The LHC, the world's most powerful collider, is too feeble by a factor of a thousand million million.

But just suppose that it is possible to make a Black Hole with the LHC. After all, as CERN itself honestly acknowledges, perhaps 'the Planck mass is not a fundamental quantity but is derived from an underlying theory with more than four space-time dimensions. In such theories the higher dimensional Planck mass may be much smaller, raising the question of whether gravitational instabilities may develop much more readily.' 'Gravitational instabilities' is polite language for Black Hole.

Doom 1: Black Hole (Part 2)

Would this Black Hole survive? No, it would evaporate because it was so small. It would give off energy. You see, contrary to popular belief, a Black Hole can evaporate and get lighter — thanks to 'Hawking Radiation'.

A Black Hole with the mass of a car (about 1,000 kg, and about 10^{-24} m in diameter) would evaporate in one billionth of a second — and during that evaporation time would be 200 times brighter than the Sun. Suppose the LHC did make a Black Hole of the Planck Length. It would evaporate in 10^{-42} seconds. A 14 TeV Black Hole (the energies involved at the LHC) would evaporate in 10^{-100} seconds.

So even if the LHC did make a Black Hole, it would evaporate in a time too short to measure.

Hawking Radiation

Hawking Radiation is radiation emitted by Black Holes. How can this be if nothing can ever leave a Black Hole? It turns out that Black Holes are not completely black but have a hint of grey about them.

Quantum Mechanics tells us that a particle and its corresponding antiparticle can pop into existence out of nothing. They can do this only if they both recombine and annihilate each other and vanish in an extremely short time. (They kind of 'borrow' energy from the vacuum, and then give it back almost immediately.)

Every now and then the particle and antiparticle will pop into reality just outside the Event Horizon of a Black Hole. On average, one will vanish into the Black Hole and one will not. So we, as external observers, will see that the Black Hole suddenly spits out a particle which has energy.

The name for this radiation is the famous 'Hawking Radiation'.

The time for a Black Hole to evaporate using this very slow mechanism is roughly the cube of its mass (in Solar Masses) multiplied by 10^{66}. So a Black Hole weighing 10 Solar Masses will need 10^{69} years to evaporate by Hawking Radiation alone. But over the eons, a Black Hole this large would have gravitationally sucked in much more than enough mass from around it to compensate for this incredibly slow rate of evaporation.

The Large Hadron Collider

The Large Hadron Collider (LHC), the biggest and most
complicated particle physics experiment ever seen.
The LHC will accelerate bunches of protons to the highest
energies ever generated by a machine, then collide them
head-on 30 million times a second.

Each collision will explode out thousands of particles
at almost the speed of light.

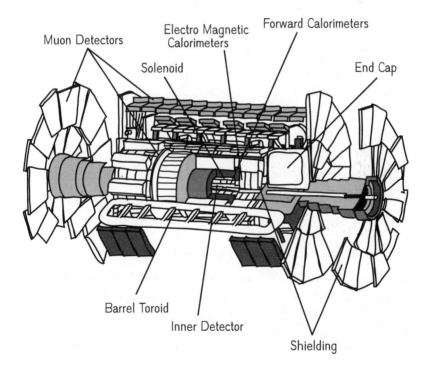

Muon Detectors

Electro Magnetic
Calorimeters

Forward Calorimeters

Solenoid

End Cap

Barrel Toroid

Inner Detector

Shielding

Doom 2: Vacuum Collapse of our Universe (Part 1)

But what about the claim that the LHC could collapse the quantum vacuum that underlies the Fabric of our Universe?

First I have to explain what this quantum vacuum is. It turns out that a vacuum is not just nothing. A vacuum is actually a seething sea of temporary particles and antiparticles, which continually pop into existence and then vanish. These particles and antiparticles exist for such a short time, before they wink out of existence again, that they don't disturb the weird laws of Quantum Physics and the Uncertainty Principle. Each particle is the exact opposite of its antiparticle — so each pair (of a particle and an antiparticle) adds up to zero. This frothing sea of short-lived particles and antiparticles is involved in making the 'zero-point energy'.

Let's pretend that we have a metal box, out of which we have sucked every single molecule of air. Even though the metal box is empty of matter, it is riddled with various energies, e.g. heat. Those energies will lessen as we cool down the box. But even if we cool our so-called vacuum down to absolute zero, we find that there is still a huge amount of energy running through the supposedly empty space. Because this energy is *still* around at absolute zero, it's called the 'zero-point energy'.

Doom 2: Vacuum Collapse of our Universe (Part 2)

It's quite easy to prove that this zero-point energy actually exists. In 1948, Hendrik B.G. Casimir from the Philips Research Laboratories in the Netherlands proposed that if you put two metal plates very close to each other, the zero-point energy would push them together!

Consider the zero-point energy in two locations — between the plates, and outside the plates. If the plates are very close together, only the very short wavelengths of energy can fit — the long wavelengths are too long to squeeze in. So between the plates, only some of the possible wavelengths of zero-point energy can happen, and they push the plates apart. But outside the plates, all the possible wavelengths of zero-point energy can happen — this energy tries to push the plates together. Casimir reckoned that there should be more energy on the outside of the plates than between them, so they should get pushed together.

In 1958, another Dutch physicist, M.J. Sparnaay, finally did the experiment in a pretty high vacuum. It turns out that if you get two metal plates, each 1 cm square, and place them 0.5 micron apart (just a fraction of the size of a human hair), the force pushing them together is equivalent to a weight of 0.2 mg. Of course, the closer the plates are together, the more of the zero-point energy of the outside Universe you can keep out, and so the force pushing the plates together is greater. And an experiment in 1996 by Steve Lamoreaux, now at Los Alamos National Laboratory in New Mexico, agreed with the predicted results to within 5%.

At the moment, we really don't know how much energy there is in the vacuum. Some scientists say that the amount of energy is insignificant, but other scientists reckon that there may be enough energy in a single cubic centimetre of vacuum to boil all the water in all the oceans on Earth. To really find out, we need to do both theory and experiment.

Crash and Burn

Two protons colliding at high speed can produce various hadrons plus very high mass particles like Z bosons.

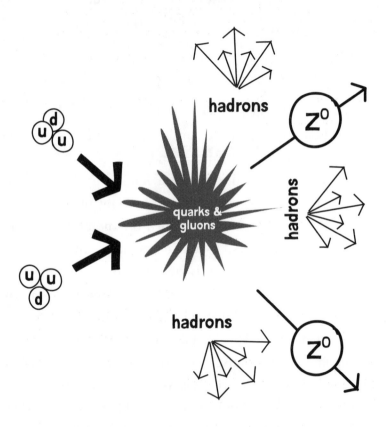

Performing these collisions may finally unveil the secret of dark matter, the mysterious entity that makes up 85% of the Universe. This would then help to explain the current mystery of the motions of galaxies.

Doom 2: Vacuum Collapse of our Universe (Part 3)

So the Universe is filled with this quantum vacuum energy. The Universe was a lot hotter soon after the Big Bang, so presumably the quantum vacuum energy was a lot greater back then. And as the Universe cooled down, then presumably the quantum vacuum energy reduced to the lowest stable level.

But what if it didn't? What if it got hung up in an energy level that is both unstable and not the lowest possible level? And what if, after a few years of operation, the LHC somehow 'kicked' the quantum vacuum a little and shoved it into the lowest possible energy level.

Perhaps a terrible wave of destruction would propagate away from the LHC in all directions, collapsing the quantum vacuum into a lower energy state — and destroying our Universe as it spreads at the speed of light.

There are two objections to this scenario — one theoretical, the other based on data.

The theoretical objection is that our scientists have already come up with various theories that describe the subatomic world very well. Our Universe is already in the correct and stable vacuum state.

The practical objection looks at cosmic rays. Cosmic rays are high-energy particles that have been hitting the solar system for all of its nearly five-billion-year history. Many of these collisions have hundreds of millions of times the maximum energies produced in the LHC. Because the quantum vacuum has survived these enormously powerful cosmic ray collisions, it should survive anything that the LHC can throw at it.

Doom 3: Strange Matter

This claim refers to 'strange matter' being accidentally created and then taking over the Universe.

'Quarks' are a type of subatomic particle that make up some of the matter in our Universe. There are six types, called 'up', 'down', 'top', 'bottom', 'charm' and yes, 'strange'. The proton (which is in every atom in the Universe) and the neutron (which is in every atom in the Universe, apart from hydrogen) are made mostly from various combinations of 'up' and 'down' quarks.

The worry here is that the LHC might accidentally create matter made from 'strange' quarks — henceforth known as 'strange matter'. When the superhot fireball cools down, it might condense into strange quarks, which might then cool down into strange matter. What if this strange matter had a natural lower energy level than regular matter? And once we had a 'seed' of strange matter, what if it set off an unstoppable chain reaction?

And what if it converted all the matter on Earth, and then the entire Universe, into strange matter. (It would work like the fictional Ice-9, in the sci-fi novel *Cat's Cradle* by Kurt Vonnegut Jr.)

Once again, there is nothing to worry about.

First, we have looked vigorously for strange matter, and have never found it anywhere in the Universe. In addition, theory tells us that strange matter is unstable in small quantities, thanks to surface effects.

Second, theory tells us that high-energy colliders like the RHIC and the LHC are a poor way to make strange matter. Low-energy colliders would be a better way — but they have been running for decades and have never produced strange matter.

Third, cosmic rays come in a wide range of energies — from much weaker than the energies produced in the LHC to hundreds of millions of times greater. Cosmic rays have not yet set off a chain reaction of strange matter conversion. Even though they have been hitting the various moons and planets in our solar system for billions of years, the moons and planets are still here.

Too Costly?

The total cost of the LHC is about US$8 billion. Yes, that is a lot of money. And yes, it is roughly the cost of three of the American B-2 stealth bombers. Each one costs about US$2.6 billion, or to be strictly accurate, US$2.595 billion, or US$2,595 million. (That's in 1996 dollars, which are worth more than today's dollars.)

My guess is that when our great-grandchildren look back to the early 21st century, they will see that the world got more benefit from the LHC, than it did from three B-2 bombers.

We're Safe, Hooray!

And even bigger energies are unleashed inside exploding nuclear weapons, inside our Sun, and around Black Holes — and the Universe has shown itself to be remarkably robust.

High-energy physics is on the verge of a major breakthrough. The LHC might find hidden extra dimensions, or the truth about the Missing Stuff that makes up 96% of the Universe, or point us towards the Quantum Theory of Gravity, or tell us why gravity is so much weaker than the other forces, or tell us where all the antimatter went. It is The Large in search of The Tiny. It could take us to the Golden Age of Physics. Or it might give us the Next Cool Thing, even better than the World Wide Web.

So let's give it a whirl and see what we find …

Black Hole = Power Pack

In the sci-fi TV series *Star Trek*, the spaceship *Enterprise* uses antimatter engines. They are efficient and do indeed convert all their fuel to pure energy.

On the other hand, the Romulan warbirds have a Black Hole (or 'artificially generated quantum singularity', as they verbosely call it) for their power supply. Black Holes have the advantage as a power pack that they are very compact (infinite density helps). This is balanced by a few disadvantages — it's not really possible to control the power output of a Black Hole, and when they run out they evaporate in an enormous blast of gamma rays.

If Black Holes did form (you know, all that extra dimension stuff), they would have a very characteristic decay signature as they evaporated, involving an electron, a muon and a photon.

If, against all odds, the LHC makes a Black Hole, and if, against all odds, we learn the technology to capture one, then it might make a nice power supply — if we can iron the bugs out of it!

References

Blaizot, J.P., et al., 'Study of Potentially Dangerous Events During Heavy-Ion Collisions at the LHC: Report of the LHC Safety Study Group', CERN, European Organization For Nuclear Research, Theoretical Physics Division, CERN 2003-001, 28 February 2003.

Dimopoulos, Savas, et al., 'Black Holes at the Large Hadron Collider', *Physical Review Letters*, 15 October 2001, Vol 87, Issue 16, pp 161602-1 to 161602-4.

'Fight to save Earth from tiny Black Hole', *Sydney Morning Herald*, 2 April 2008, p 9.

Jaffe, R.L., et al., 'Review of speculative "disaster scenarios" at RHIC', *Reviews of Modern Physics*, 1 October 2000, Vol 72, Issue 4, pp 1125–1140.

Kolbert, Elizabeth, 'Crash Course: Can a seventeen-mile-long collider unlock the Universe?', *The New Yorker*, 14 May 2007.

Leake, Jonathan, 'Big Bang machine could destroy Earth', *The Sunday Times* (London), 18 July 1999.

Matthews, Robert, 'A Black Hole ate my planet', *New Scientist*, 28 August 1999.

Muir, Hazel, 'Dark destroyers', New Scientist, *Inside Science* No 154, 19 October 2002, Insert pp 1–4.

Mukerjee, Madhusree, 'A little Big Bang', *Scientific American*, March 1999, pp 60–65.

Overbye, Dennis, 'A giant takes on Physics' biggest questions', *The New York Times*, 15 May 2007.

Parikh, Maulik K., et al., 'Hawking Radiation as tunneling', *Physical Review Letters*, 11 December 2000, Vol 85, Issue 24, pp 5042–5045.

Walker, Gabrielle, 'The biggest thing in Physics', *Discover Magazine*, 13 August 2007, pp 45–49.

Black Holes Don't Suck

'Black Hole'! The name certainly conjures up the image of a sci-fi menace. Black Holes are truly strange 'places' where the Laws of Physics are turned completely inside out. And the expression 'Black Hole' has now eclipsed the 'Bottomless Pit' as something that takes, and takes, and takes — and never gives anything back.

Most of us wrongly believe that Black Holes are a kind of Cosmic Vacuum Cleaner, sucking everything around them into their voracious maw. The truth is that if the Sun were to be replaced by a Black Hole with the same mass as the Sun, the Earth would still maintain the same orbit — and would not get sucked in.

Black Holes come in a range of sizes, from possibly the size of an atom to about ten times bigger than our solar system. The largest one known is about 18 billion Solar Masses. (A 'Solar Mass' is an astronomical unit of mass equal to the mass of our Sun, i.e. 2×10^{30}kg.)

The American Association of Astronomers states that practically every galaxy has a Black Hole at its centre. There's a massive one of about 3.7 million Solar Masses located about 26,000 light years away at the centre of our galaxy, the Milky Way.

But right next door to it (only a few light years away) is another Black Hole. It's much smaller, only about 1,300 Solar Masses. And there are probably a few million smaller ones scattered throughout our galaxy.

The path to understanding Black Holes has been long and hard, earning scientists several Nobel Prizes.

A Few Numbers

Diameter of Sun = 1.4 million km

Mass of Sun = 2×10^{30} kg = 1 Solar Mass

Diameter of Earth = 12,750 km

Mass of Earth = 6×10^{24} kg

Mass of Moon = 7×10^{22} kg

Distance from Sun to Earth = 1 Astronomical Unit = 150 million km = 8.3 light minutes = 1AU

Distance from Sun to Pluto = 29–49 AU = 4.4–7.4 billion km. Average distance of 5.9 billion km = 5.5 light hours = 40 AU

Distance to Nearest Star, Proxima Centauri = 4.42 light years

Distance to centre of Milky Way = 26,000 light years

Diameter of Milky Way = 100,000 light years

Age of Universe = 13.7 billion years

Age of Sun = 4.6 billion years

Speed of Light = 300,000 km/sec

Nucleus of an atom = $2\text{–}12 \times 10^{-15}$ m

Entire atoms = about $100{,}000 \times 10^{-15}$ m

Black Holes

A Black Hole is a region of Space in which the gravitational field is so powerful that nothing, not even light, can escape its pull after having fallen past its event horizon.

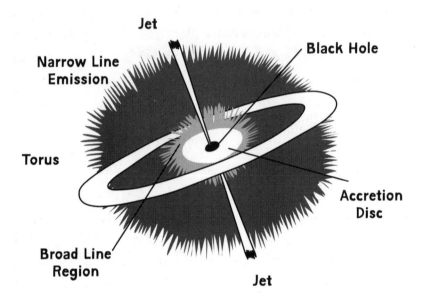

The anatomy of a Black Hole

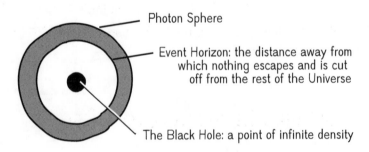

A static Black Hole

History of Black Hole Concept

In 1783, the British clergyman and amateur geologist/scientist, Reverend John Michell, started the Black Hole ball rolling. He wondered about a body in Space falling towards a truly huge star, say 500 times the size of the Sun (which is about 1.4 million km in diameter). In a letter to his friend Henry Cavendish (the English chemist and physicist who in 1798 made the first accurate measurement of the density of the Earth), which was published by The Royal Society, Michell stated that 'a body falling from an infinite height towards it would have acquired at its surface greater velocity than that of light, and consequently … all light emitted from such a body would be made to return towards it by its own proper gravity'.

Scientists already knew that objects had gravity, and that this gravity would attract other objects. But back then, nobody knew if gravity would affect something as wispy and ephemeral as light. John Michell must have been a deep thinker to ponder such a bizarre concept. He called this heavy star a 'Dark Star', because if all the light that it emitted were sucked back by its own gravity, it would be 'dark'.

Soon after, in around 1795, the brilliant French astronomer and mathematician Pierre Simon, Marquis de Laplace, independently came up with the same concept of light interacting with enormously massive objects.

Gravity is Just Curved Space

At this time, scientists did not really believe that gravity would affect light. But in 1915, Albert Einstein published his 'General Theory of Relativity' in which ten equations known as Einstein's Field Equations describe the fundamental force of gravitation as curved Space-Time and energy. Einstein said that the Fabric of Space-Time was made up of three space dimensions (left–right, backwards–forwards and up–down, or if you have studied high-school geometry, x, y and z) and one time dimension (that usually ticks away at one second per second). The special properties of Space-Time limits what you can do. For example, you always have to move forward in time, and you can't shift matter or information faster than the speed of light.

Einstein said that a mass (such as a star) would warp or twist this Fabric of Space-Time. Think of the Fabric of Space-Time as being like a sheet of rubber. In empty Space with no objects to provide mass, the sheet is flat. But a star has mass, and this mass somehow curves the local Space-Time. A star makes a big dent in the rubber sheet, a planet makes a medium-sized dent and a small asteroid makes a tiny one. Light just follows the Fabric of Space-Time — running across the dents and bumps in the Fabric. This is how and why light is affected by gravity.

In 1916, the physicist and astronomer Karl Schwarzschild was the first to discover exact solutions to some of Einstein's Field Equations. Black Holes were a part of his bizarre mathematical solutions — in fact, they are an essential part of the solutions of Einstein's Field Equations. But even Einstein thought that this was just a mathematical accident, and in no way related to the real Universe, as he believed that stars could never shrink small enough to make a Black Hole.

The thinking all began to change in 1967 when the first Neutron Star was discovered by Jocelyn Bell and Antony Hewish. This proved that strange ultra-dense objects actually do exist in the Universe.

The structure of a Neutron Star is very strange. Its 'atmosphere' is made of ordinary atoms (such as those found on Earth) and electrons — but is only about one metre thick! It has a solid crust

Curved space bends light

'Put your hand on a hot stove for a minute
and it seems like an hour. Sit with a pretty girl for an hour
and it seems like a minute. That's relativity.' Einstein

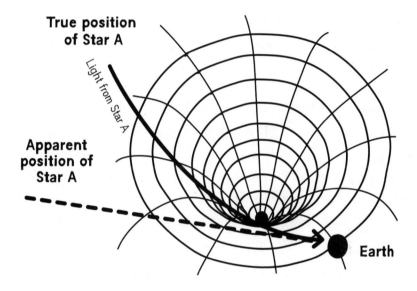

**True position
of Star A**

Light from Star A

**Apparent
position of
Star A**

Earth

In this diagram the Space-Time fabric of our solar system is
seen bent by the gravitational force of the Sun.
In the absence of a gravitational field, light travels along
a straight path (dotted line of Star A). A gravitational field
produced by a massive object will bend the trajectory of
the light ray (Star A) like a ball rolling along a warped table.

about 1.5 km thick, under which everything is 'liquid'. But it's a very strange 'liquid' — mostly naked neutrons, and about a hundred million to a billion times denser than a White Dwarf (a small faint star of enormous density, which itself is a million times denser than water). This gives a Neutron Star an escape velocity of about half the speed of light, with a surface gravity about a million million times greater than that experienced on Earth.

One way to understand these ultra-dense objects is to consider the workings of 'escape velocity'.

Escape Velocity

In 1783, John Michell was using the concept of 'escape velocity', i.e. the velocity needed to 'escape' from a gravity well.

Here's how it works. If you throw a rock upwards, pretty soon it falls back down again. If you throw it upwards ten times faster, the rock takes longer to fall down — but it will still fall back to Earth. But if you propel the rock up with a speed of 11.2 km/sec, it will never fall back down to Earth. So the 'escape velocity' of planet Earth is 11.2 km/sec (or approximately 40,300 kph).

A Black Hole has such a massive density compared to its size, that its escape velocity is equal to the speed of light, or even greater. This means that light itself can never escape. In other words, we can never see it, hence the name 'Black Hole'.

History of the Name 'Black Hole'

In 1964, Ann Ewing wrote for the 18 January issue of *Science News Letter* about a meeting of the American Association for the Advancement of Science. Part of the meeting was about astrophysics. She wrote: 'According to Einstein's general theory of relativity, as mass is added to a degenerate star a sudden collapse will take place and the intense gravitational field of the star will close in on itself. Such a star then forms a "black hole" in the universe.'

And in 1967, according to the *Scientific American*, the famous physicist John Wheeler popularised the phrase in a public lecture called 'Our Universe: The Known and Unknown'. 'Wheeler recalls discussing such "completely collapsed gravitational objects" at a conference in 1967, when someone in the audience casually dropped the phrase "black hole". Wheeler immediately adopted the phrase for its brevity and "advertising value" …' Well, one thing is sure — 'Black Hole' is certainly a lot easier to say than 'completely collapsed gravitational object'.

Black Hole Formation

In many cases, a Black Hole evolved from a star. Stars are born in a 'Stellar Nursery' as protostars. A small protostar of less than 0.075 Solar Masses will turn into a Brown Dwarf. A heavier protostar (between 0.075 and 0.5 Solar Masses) will then get hot enough for nuclear burning to become a Red Dwarf. A protostar between 0.5 and 8 Solar Masses will eventually turn into a White Dwarf.

But a star's final evolution is very different if it starts off quite massive, say, more than about 20–25 Solar Masses. After the protostar stage, it lives as a large star, about 5 million km in diameter. It will burn hydrogen for about ten million years, and then expand to about 50 million km in diameter. It will then burn helium in its core for about one million years, and expand enormously to about 700 million km in diameter. (Just for comparison, in our solar system, the Earth is about 150 million km from the Sun, while Mars is about 225 million km away from the Sun.) It will burn its way quickly up the Periodic Table, getting through carbon, neon, oxygen and silicon in just 1,000 years, until

Burning — Nuclear or Chemical

Chemical burning is something we see all the time — in a forest fire where the carbon in the trees combines with the oxygen in the atmosphere, or on a gas stove where the carbon in the methane gas combines with the surrounding oxygen in the atmosphere. In each case, carbon combines with oxygen to give carbon dioxide and energy (usually heat).

Nuclear burning is very different in two ways.

First, it doesn't need any oxygen. Instead, two elements combine to give a third element (and sometimes a fourth). For example, two hydrogen atoms combine to make a helium atom. But the mass of the atom of helium produced is slightly less than the mass of the two hydrogen atoms. There is some mass missing. This mass is converted directly into energy. (You can work out how much by Einstein's famous equation, $E = mc^2$, where 'E' is the energy produced, 'm' is the mass that is turned into energy and 'c' is the speed of light.)

Second, nuclear burning delivers absolutely enormous amounts of energy, much much more than chemical burning.

it gets to iron. Once it gets to iron, the nuclear furnace is extinguished, because getting to elements heavier than iron needs an input of energy. Now that the nuclear fires are out, there is no longer any outward rush of radiation. So the star collapses, releasing a huge amount of gravitational energy, and explodes.

After all the nuclear burning, we now have a collapsing star weighing more than approximately 2.5 Solar Masses. In this case, it will shrink so far that it will collapse into a point with infinite density and zero volume.

A Star is Born

Stars are born in what astronomers call a 'Stellar Nursery'.
This is a much more romantic name than a Giant Molecular
Cloud (GMC), but they are the same thing.

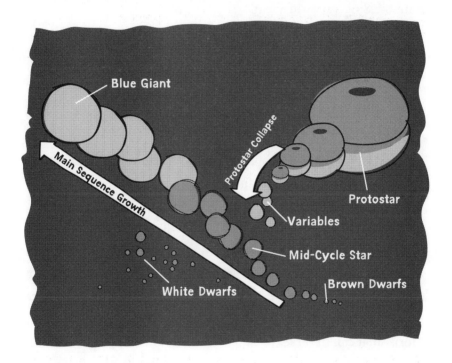

This is a simplified diagram of how stellar evolution begins.
The first stage is the formation of a Protostar, which is a
large vortex of dust and gas that accumulates matter. This
large star will collapse into a variable star, which eventually
settles down into a main sequence star and will continue to
accrete matter as long as the supply lasts.

Let me just emphasise that the density is not just colossally high, but *infinite*. And the volume is not just very small, but *zero*.

The technical name for this 'thing' with infinite density and zero volume is a 'Singularity' — but the popular name is 'Black Hole'. And this point in Space is hidden inside what is called the Event Horizon.

By the way, the term 'Black Hole' is a little ambiguous — it can refer just to the Singularity or, more usually, to the Event Horizon with the Singularity inside it.

Event Horizon

Black Holes don't actually have a physical surface, but instead they have the so-called Event Horizon — the point of no return — which has the shape of a sphere around its central Black Hole. At the Event Horizon, the escape velocity is equal to the speed of light.

Inside the Event Horizon, every ray of light, and every possible particle of matter, has to take a path towards the Singularity. The Space-Time Fabric inside an Event Horizon is curved in such a way that all roads lead to the Singularity. For that reason, once anything (light, any other energy, or matter) crosses the Event Horizon, it can never leave, and is doomed to end up at the central Singularity.

Suppose that our Sun was magically compressed so that its density got high enough to set off the gravitational collapse that would lead to infinite density and a Singularity or Black Hole. The Singularity would have zero volume. But the Event Horizon would be 3 km away. It is not a physical space or barrier — in fact, if you were falling into a supermassive Black Hole, you would hardly notice crossing the Event Horizon on the way into the Black Hole.

Sizes of Black Holes

It seems that Black Holes can cover a range of sizes, from the microscopic to the super supermassive.

But how do you measure the size of a Black Hole when it is just a point in Space with mass and zero volume? Well, you forget the Singularity, and just calculate the size of the Event Horizon. The exact formula for the Schwarzschild Radius of the Event Horizon of a non-rotating, non-charged Black Hole is given by:

$$r_{sh} \text{ (km)} = 2GM/c^2$$

where 'G' is Newton's Constant of Gravity, 'M' is the mass of the Black Hole and 'c' is the speed of light.

But a simple approximation for the radius is:

$$r_{sh} \text{ (km)} = 3 \times \text{mass of Black Hole/mass of Sun}$$

So if you had a Black Hole with the mass of the Sun, the Event Horizon would have a radius of 3 km. But Black Holes seem to come in all sizes. A Black Hole with the mass of the Earth would have an Event Horizon 18 mm in diameter.

Black Holes — Supermassive or Heart of Darkness

Black Holes come in all sizes, so let's begin with the Big Mothers.

Most of these range from 100,000 to one billion Solar Masses, with sizes ranging from 600,000 km to 6 billion km in diameter.

The biggest known Black Hole so far clocks in at 18 billion Solar Masses and goes under the name of OJ 287. Part of a binary Black Hole system, its companion is about 200 times less massive, only (!) 90 million Solar Masses.

Sgr A* (see also p 245), the Black Hole at the middle of our galaxy, the Milky Way, is about 3.7 million Solar Masses (about 20 million km in diameter). Most Black Holes at the centre of galaxies have major bursts of activity (such as cataclysmic blasts of X-rays) every few days. But Sgr A* is very quiet at the moment, with hardly any activity — it's almost on a starvation diet. However, about 350 years ago, it was gobbling stars and frantically gulping and slurping huge clouds of gas and other matter at the rate of a million million tonnes per second — and it did this for about ten years. It was also blasting out huge amounts of gamma radiation, which hit an enormous gas cloud, called Sig B2, about 350 light years from Sgr A*. After this gas cloud absorbed the gamma rays, it then began emitting vast quantities of X-rays which are only now hitting Earth.

A galaxy (NGC 6240) that is not too far away (only 400 million light years) seems to have two supermassive Black Holes — it has two Hearts of Darkness. They are each between 10 and 100 Solar Masses and are about 3,000 light years apart. In only a few hundred million years, they will collide with each other to make an even bigger Black Hole and release an awesomely large blast of gravitational waves. (Strangely, if you smash two enormous Black Holes together, you do not destroy them — you just get one super-enormous Black Hole.) Mathematicians also tell us that it's possible for the newly formed Black Hole to be booted entirely out of the mother galaxy.

We still don't have a good theory of how these supermassive Black Holes are made. Perhaps they are made from the repeated collisions of smaller Black Holes, or perhaps they are very hungry and eat lots of gas, dust and entire stars (a more likely theory, for various reasons). Or perhaps they were made in the so-called 'Dark Age', a period of time about 400 million years long that lies between the cooling down from the Big Bang and the beginning of star formation, when immense stars were thought to have lived fast and died young. Or perhaps they grow when two galaxies collide — when there are many tasty morsels of stars, gas and dust there for the eating.

How Many Black Holes Are There?

The Chandra X-Ray Telescope has given us a rough answer. Nothing can leave the Event Horizon — but as stuff falls in, it can give off X-rays as it picks up speed and crashes into other infalling material. The Chandra X-Ray Telescope looked at an unspectacular and boring part of the sky, roughly two-thirds of the size of the full Moon. Over a two-year period, it built up a total of about 23 days of staring at this tiny area of sky. (Time on any big telescope is very precious. Astronomers can only book time on a telescope in little bursts here and there.) Chandra found that most of what we thought was the fuzzy even X-ray background of the sky was actually made up of individual 'points' that give off X-rays. So there are at least 300 million Black Holes in the heavens — and almost certainly, a whole lot more.

Black Holes — Intermediate

These Black Holes have an average size of around 1,000 Solar Masses, with Event Horizons ranging from 1,000 to 12,000 km. They are lighter than supermassive Black Holes, but heavier than Stellar Mass Black Holes that are born in the death throes of a massive star. Until a decade ago, we were not even sure that they existed.

One of these, IRS 13E, is about three light years from Sgr A* (the supermassive Black Hole at the centre of our Milky Way galaxy). It has about 1,300 Solar Masses and is located within a rotating and moving, tightly packed cluster of six massive stars, just 24 light days across.

Some of these intermediate-size Black Holes also occur in globular clusters.

Globular clusters are tightly bound dense groups of stars, with hundreds of thousands of stars clustered close together. They spin slowly with the rest of the galaxy, but usually a fair way out from the centre. The first one was discovered in 1665. There are about 200 globular clusters in our Milky Way. In the globular cluster called M15, which is about 32,000 light years away, there's a Black Hole of 4,000 Solar Masses. And in the Andromeda Galaxy, about 2.2 million light years away, in the globular cluster called G1, there's a Black Hole of 20,000 Solar Masses.

Could it be that the stars in a globular cluster are so tightly packed that collisions between the stars can create these intermediate-size Black Holes?

Once again, we don't really have a good theoretical mechanism for how these Black Holes are made. And we don't know how they relate to the supermassive Black Hole at the core of the galaxy. Perhaps IRS 13E is one of a bunch of intermediate-size Black Holes that go out on highly elliptical orbits and bring back food for the supermassive Black Hole in the centre of the galaxy — and when Big Mother is not looking, they quietly nibble off a few stars to keep themselves running!

Binary Stars

A binary star system has two stars going around their common centre of gravity, 'held' together by their common gravitational attraction. It turns out that our solar system (with just one star) is quite unusual. About 75% of all stars are in multiple systems, the majority being binary! And about 10% of multiple systems have more than two stars. Back in 1802, Sir William Herschel was one of the first to define them as 'a real double star — the union of two stars that are formed together in one system by the laws of attraction'.

Black Holes — Stellar

We do have theoretical mechanisms for 'making' Stellar Black Holes. They start off as stars of more than 20–40 Solar Masses and turn into Black Holes after the nuclear fires go out. They can also form from the collision of two Neutron Stars, or from matter falling onto the surface of a Neutron Star. These Black Holes have masses ranging from 2.5 to 20 Solar Masses and are about 15–120 km in diameter.

There are many Black Holes in this size range known in our, and other, galaxies. In almost all cases, they are one of the two stars in a binary star system. (This is probably because a Black Hole in a binary system is easier to find than a solitary Black Hole.)

The first Black Hole ever to be discovered was Cygnus X-1.

X-rays from Outer Space are blocked by our atmosphere. So in 1964, X-ray instrumentation was loaded into a small sounding rocket which was sent into Space. In its brief time outside the atmosphere, the X-ray instruments found something very bright in the constellation Cygnus, about 6,000 light years from Earth. Over the years since then, increasingly sophisticated X-ray telescopes have been launched. And we now know that Black Holes often show up as points of X-ray energy. Thanks to the data collected with these instruments, by 1990 scientists were pretty sure that Cygnus X-1 is a small invisible (invisible with light, but visible with X-rays) Stellar Black Hole in a binary system. It probably formed about five million years ago from a star of 40 Solar Masses.

How Do You Find Black Holes?

Here's a question. If a Black Hole is invisible, and it's very small as well, then how can you find it? The answer lies in the knowledge that a Black Hole has a gravitational field — and you can actually observe the effects of this gravitational field.

We have found a Black Hole at the core of virtually every galaxy that we have closely examined. A Black Hole makes up about 0.5% of the mass of its host galaxy. Stars, gas and dust are seen orbiting the core — and do so very, very quickly.

One way to find Black Holes is to look for the X-rays given off by the fast-moving gas. As gas gets pulled in towards the Black Hole, it gains huge amounts of kinetic energy and gets very hot. In turn, the heat makes the infalling matter give off a rather characteristic pattern of X-rays, which we have actually detected. We have found many cases of a fast-moving visible star orbiting very quickly around an invisible and massive object, which has lots of these characteristic X-rays coming off it, i.e. a Black Hole.

Another method was used by Rainer Schödel from the Max Planck Institute for Extraterrestrial Physics in Germany, and his co-workers in Germany, France, Israel and the USA. They used Newton's Laws of Gravity and Kepler's Laws (discovered some 400 years ago), to 'weigh' the Black Hole at the centre of our galaxy.

Schödel and his colleagues looked at a star of 15 Solar Masses, called S2, that orbits around a 'mysterious' object at the centre of our galaxy. Astronomers call this object Sagittarius A* (or Sgr A*), and for various reasons they have long thought it to be a Black Hole. For example, this object emits the sort of X-ray radiation that we would expect from a Black Hole.

The orbit of S2 is very elliptical — 17 light hours from Sgr A* at its very closest, and 11 light days at its most distant. S2 has been monitored for many years, and we now know that it takes 15.2 years to do a complete orbit.

S2 is a lot further out from the core of our galaxy than Pluto is from the Sun, but orbits much more quickly. The reason why S2 is moving so rapidly is because it is trying to avoid being gravitationally sucked in by something that weighs 3.7 million times the mass of our Sun.

Just about the only object that could weigh so much and be so small is a Black Hole. This kind of data makes us pretty sure that Black Holes do exist.

The other star in the binary system is a supergiant blue star, known as HDE 226868. It is very hot (with a surface temperature of 31,000 Kelvin), massive (about 30 Solar Masses) and huge (30 million km in diameter, or about 20 times bigger than our Sun).

Because it is so massive, it is shedding mass at the rate of one Solar Mass every 400,000 years. Normally, it would eject this material in all directions. But the combination of the *intense gravity* and the *closeness* of Cygnus X-1 Black Hole means that most of the ejected material from the blue supergiant is captured by Cygnus X-1.

By 'intense gravity', I mean that Cygnus X-1 weighs in at about 8.7 Solar Masses (so it's too massive to be a Neutron Star, which has a limit of about 2.5 Solar Masses). And by 'closeness', I mean that the Black Hole, Cygnus X-1, is 45 million km from the centre of the supergiant blue star, i.e. it sits practically on top of the blue supergiant. The distance between the centres of the two stars is just one-and-a-half times the size of the blue supergiant. The twostars (the Black Hole and the blue supergiant) are in a very tight orbit

Measuring Temperature

Most of us know about measuring temperature in degrees Celsius or degrees Fahrenheit.

However, scientists tend to use Kelvin (not degrees Kelvin, just Kelvin — and yes, the name is related to the Kelvinator refrigerator, and Lord Kelvin, the British physicist and mathematician who invented the Kelvin scale).

A Kelvin is the same 'size' as a Celsius degree.
So 1 K = 1°C = 1.8°F.

But Kelvin and Celsius have different starting points. Zero Kelvin is also called 'Absolute Zero', and is equal to −273.15°C, while 0°C is equal to +273.15 K. Once the temperatures reach hundreds of thousands or millions of Kelvins, 273.15 does not make a lot of difference, so astronomers tend to talk about 'millions of degrees' and leave out the K or the C.

around each other. But because the two stars are quite massive, the time needed for a complete orbit is just 5.6 days.

Very strange things happen to the gas that the Black Hole sucks off the supergiant blue star. As it leaves the surface of the supergiant, it gets pulled into a teardrop shape and then narrows into a thin stream, which then gets sucked into Cygnus X-1's Event Horizon. It then spirals around the Black Hole before falling in, taking on the shape of a disc around the Black Hole. The technical name for this is an 'accretion disc'.

But something else happens. The gas picks up huge amounts of energy as it falls towards the Event Horizon. Some of this energy is given off by enormous jets of particles, moving at significant fractions of the speed of light, and lined up at right angles to the accretion disc. The amount of power inherent in these jets is stupendous — about 1,000 times more than our Sun emits. And of course, the jet also gives off huge amounts of X-rays.

Given that there are about 400 billion stars in our galaxy, and that stars bigger than 20–40 Solar Masses end up as Black Holes, there must already be millions of stellar-size Black Holes in the Milky Way.

Black Holes — Tiny

It is theoretically possible for a tiny Black Hole to continue to exist, once it has been made.

Unfortunately, we don't have any theoretical mechanism to say how they can be made. They might have been produced in the titanic energies of the Big Bang but would have 'evaporated' by now. Or perhaps they could be made in the Large Hadron Collider (LHC) — but again, they would evaporate in blindingly short times. (Read more about the Large Hadron Collider in the chapter 'Crash Collider: LHC Destroys Universe'.)

What's the Matter ?

This diagram shows Matter being torn from the Black Hole's companion star to form a hot, swirling accretion disc.

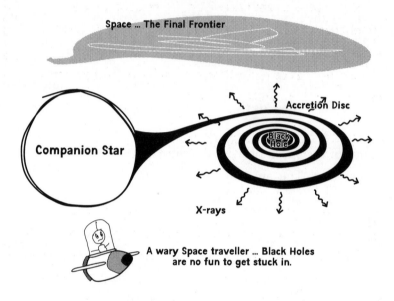

Space ... The Final Frontier

Accretion Disc

Black Hole

Companion Star

X-rays

A wary Space traveller ... Black Holes are no fun to get stuck in.

Low mass Black Holes can be very small indeed. A Black Hole with the mass of the Moon would be about 0.2 mm across, about half the size of the head of a pin.

The Big Conclusion

If our Sun were to be 'magically' turned into a Black Hole with its current mass, it would be a lot smaller than it is as a star. The Event Horizon would be about 6 km in diameter. Close to the Event Horizon — about 3 km away from the Singularity — the gravitational field would increase enormously. But far away from the Event Horizon (say, a few thousand kilometres) the Black Hole

Black Hole Bart

Black Holes are mentioned in movies, books, and even poems. But the highest praise possible in Western society is to be part of the plot of an episode of *The Simpsons*.

Black Holes starred heavily in the episode called 'Treehouse of Horror' (Season 7, Episode 6, which had three short stories, the third being Homer³). In Homer³, Homer tries to hide from Marge's sisters when they come to visit, and ends up falling into a Black Hole. As he falls in, he yells out, 'There's so much I don't know about astrophysics. I wish I'd read that book by the wheelchair guy', referring to Stephen Hawking the British physicist (who is confined to a wheelchair).

Even more impressively, Stephen Hawking himself actually has a speaking part as a guest in the episode 'Don't Fear the Roofer' (Season 16, Episode 16). Hawking suggests to Bart that a small Black Hole in front of Homer's friend, Ray the Roofer, is absorbing all the light, so that Bart can't see Ray.

would have the same gravitational field as the Sun — because it would still have the same mass. The only real difference to us is that it would be cold and dark, because the Black Hole would not emit any heat or light.

If an object such as a comet, or even a planet, were on a collision course with the Event Horizon, yes, it would vanish inside the Black Hole. But this is just a normal property of gravity. If you are not orbiting fast enough around either a Black Hole or a regular star, you will get sucked in. So if a comet or planet started off in a stable orbit around the Sun, then it would continue in the same stable orbit after the Sun had been magically turned into a Black Hole. After all, there are hundreds of billions of stars in the Milky Way, all orbiting around the supermassive Black Hole in the centre. Apart from a very few stars very close to the centre, they will not get sucked in and will continue to orbit around this 3.7-million-Solar-Mass Black Hole.

If the Sun did become a Black Hole, the only way that the Earth could fall in would be if it lost 99.99% of its orbital angular momentum.

Black Holes are very weird, and up close to them, some of the normal rules of the Universe are turned around. But they do not suck everything into themselves.

However, as with all the Forces of Darkness, it's better to stay out of their way.

References

Begelman, Mitchell C., 'Evidence for Black Holes', *Science*, 20 June 2003, Vol 300, No 5627, pp 1898–1904.

Cowen, R., 'Hole in the middle: Are midsize Black Holes the missing link?', *Science News*, 21 September 2001, Vol 162, No 12, p 180.

Gebhardt, Karl, 'Into the heart of darkness', *Nature*, 17 October 2002, pp 675–676.

Hellemans, Alexander, 'X-rays show a Galaxy can have two hearts', *Science*, 29 November 2002, Vol 298, No 5599, p 1698.

Iorio, Lorenzo, 'On the orbital and physical parameters of the HDE 226868/Cygnus X-1 binary system', *Astrophysics and Space Science*, June 2008, 315: 1– 4, pp 335–340.

Maillard, J.P., et al., 'The nature of the Galactic Center source IRS 13 revealed by high spatial resolution in the infrared', *Astronomy & Astrophysics*, August 2004, Vol 423, pp 155–167.

Muir, Hazel, 'Our Black Hole may be sleeping now', *New Scientist*, 5 February 2005, p 8.

Schödel, R., et al., 'A star in a 15.2-year orbit around the supermassive Black Hole at the centre of the Milky Way', *Nature*, 17 October 2002, pp 694–696.

Thomas, Vanessa, 'Dark heart of a Globular', *Astronomy*, January 2003, p 32.

Valtonen, M.J., et al., 'A massive binary Black-Hole system in OJ 287 and a test of general relativity', *Nature*, 17 April 2008, pp 851–853.

Acknowledgments

I would like to thank the various experts who were kind enough to give me some of their deep wisdom, and read and comment on some of my little stories that touch on their field of knowledge. Of course, if any mistakes do remain (and remember the old saying, 'If you don't make a mistake, you don't make anything'), I accept full responsibility and will correct them in subsequent printings of this book.

Professor Helen Muir of Cranfield University was kind enough to look at 'Plane Truths' (i.e. you are quite likely to survive a plane crash). All the other experts are from the University of Sydney. Professor Rosanne Taylor from the Faculty of Veterinary Science looked at 'Sweat Like a Pig', while Professor Geraint Lewis from the School of Physics looked at 'Black Holes Don't Suck', and Dr Kevin Varvell from the School of Physics looked at 'Crash Collider: LHC Destroys Universe'.

I would also like to thank the fine people at the *Good Weekend* (Saturday supplement to the *Sydney Morning Herald* and *The Age*) for helping through the 12-or-so hours that it took to write each of the original 400-word stories that appeared in my 'Mythconceptions' column, and Dan Driscoll from the ABC for turning them into Street Talk.

Other Dr Karl titles

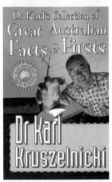

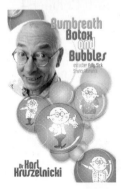